THE BIRDS

the Birds

by Oskar Heinroth and Katharina Heinroth

ANN ARBOR
THE UNIVERSITY OF MICHIGAN PRESS

66-4712

Third printing 1962

*Published in the United States of America by
The University of Michigan Press and simultaneously
in Toronto, Canada, by Ambassador Books Limited*

Library of Congress Catalog Card No. 58-62521

First published as Aus Dem Leben Der Voegel, *second enlarged
edition 1955 by Springer-Verlag, Berlin–Goettingen–Heidelberg.*

Translated by Michael Cullen

Designed by George Lenox

Printed in the United States of America

Contents

THE BIRDS

1. *What Is a Bird?*

The saying "You can tell a bird by its feathers" is literally true. Not only are birds the only living creatures to wear feathers, but the feathers themselves differ greatly according to whether their wearer lives in water, in marshy country, in dry grassland, or in desert. Water birds, and especially penguins, have feathers which cover the whole body almost like scales. In gamebirds and others, the feathers are arranged in tracts in the skin, but in such a way that none of the skin is left uncovered. Others—such as the ostrich, the turkey, and many vultures—have naked patches of skin. In every case the plumage serves, like the fur of mammals, chiefly for protection against cold, for birds are the most warm-blooded of animals and can therefore live in the coldest regions of the world in spite of their small size. A body temperature of 107.6° F. is about average for many birds; some species average around 113° F., which would be a deadly fever heat for a man. The fossil, lizard-like bird *Archaeopteryx*, from the Upper Jurassic period, had feathers, which shows that it was warm-blooded.

It has recently been found that the temperature of certain birds occasionally falls very low and that the birds become torpid. When the poorwill hibernates in this way, its temperature may drop to 65° F. Some hummingbirds and swifts become torpid for a few hours or days and can in this way survive times when they cannot get food.

FIG. 1. *Archaeopteryx.* Lizard-like fossil bird from the Upper Jurassic period. About one-seventh natural size.

The feathers of ostriches, cassowaries, and emus have become modified, losing the typical broad vane with its interlocking branches and becoming fluffy instead. But they are still just as much true feathers as the hair-like whiskers around the mouths of many Old World fly-catchers and nightjars; these feathers have been reduced to bare shafts.

There are about 8,600 species of birds, and about three times as many forms if you count the finer geographical varieties known as races. We humans notice birds far more than other animals chiefly because they are day animals like ourselves and are active and volatile creatures which do not hide themselves in holes at the slightest danger. We continually see them in movement, hopping among the branches, running on the ground, scuttling in the reeds, swimming or diving in the water, or soaring overhead in the sky. Because they can easily escape from their enemies they need not keep quiet like their neighbors the mammals, and so we are more familiar with them.

In the winter when most of the small insect folk become sluggish or die, many of the birds which feed on them migrate southward to winter in warmer climates. But those that stay behind become much more conspicuous to us when the leaves fall from the trees, and in addition their numbers are swollen by newly arrived immigrants from the North.

All birds lay eggs, like their ancestors the reptiles. (In Australia there are even egg-laying mammals!) Unlike most reptiles birds hatch theirs by brooding or incubating them. The parent bird not only guards the eggs, as do many fishes, but it warms them with the heat of its body. In fact the word "brood" is connected with the idea of heating.

FIG. 2. Compare this skeleton of the coucal with Figure 1. The two are laid out in the same way. About one-seventh natural size.

FIG. 3. and FIG. 4. Vasa parrot which did not get new feathers after molting. $T =$ Tarsal joint, $K =$ Knee, $F =$ Forearm, $W =$ Wrist, $Th =$ Thumb, $E =$ Elbow. About one-sixth natural size.

The forelimbs of birds are never used for walking, though the South American hoatzin when it is young has little claws on its wings which help it to scramble about the nesting tree. Birds have turned their front legs into wings, which most of them use for flight. In ratite birds (ostriches, rheas, emus, cassowaries, and moas), some rails, and a few other birds the wings have become completely useless (although the ostrich uses his for display), while the penguin's have been transformed into paddles for swimming (Fig. 79).

The bird's body is designed to fly. In almost all species many of the bones are hollow, and the body is streamlined so that it cuts through the air with its beak, becomes broadest at the breast, and tapers gradually to the tail. People are amazed at how ugly a naked bird looks (Figs. 3 and 4).

When the layman thinks of "a bird" he usually imagines the sort of sparrow-thrush that children draw. He forgets the ducks and geese, the flamingos, penguins, grebes, and hummingbirds, and the dozens of other families; so he has a very one-sided picture of the feathered world. When he wants to think about the special equipment of birds he does not consider the remarkable filter-beak of certain ducks and flamingos, the beautiful diving apparatus of penguins and grebes, or the peculiar wing of hummingbirds. And he knows just as little about the voices of birds, how they build their nests, how they take care of their young, or how they think.

These general remarks may seem unnecessary, but we must realize from the beginning that there is no such animal as The Bird; it is merely an abstraction crystallized from a rich variety of life-forms. Let us then beware of generalizations and keep in mind that what is true of a pair of blue tits does not necessarily apply to an Australian brushturkey. The person who knows only a few species always makes the mistake at first of assuming that what he has seen in one bird is true of others. The experienced ornithologist is astonished by the many different ways in which different species solve a particular problem, each in accordance with its own structure and habits and each in a more or less unvarying and instinctive way. This book is intended to give some idea of this variety.

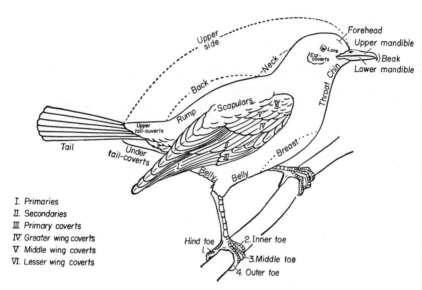

I. Primaries
II. Secondaries
III. Primary coverts
IV. Greater wing coverts
V. Middle wing coverts
VI. Lesser wing coverts

FIG. 5a. The parts of the bird.

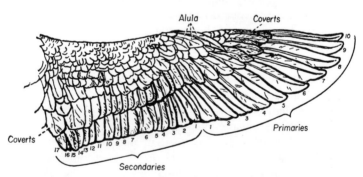

FIG. 5b. Wing of a graylag goose seen from above.

2. *The Nest*

The great majority of birds build nests in which they lay and incubate their eggs. Many, though by no means all, also use the nest as a cradle to rear the helpless young after they have hatched. But the roosting place of an adult bird is very seldom a nest: only woodpeckers, some songbirds (or passerines, as they are often called), and a few others build nests to sleep in.

When you read that The Bird hurries home to its nest at the approach of night (or rain or thunderstorms), your author is indulging in poetry; except in the breeding season few birds have any precise home.

Then where does a bird spend the night? Towards nightfall many of them travel considerable distances to particular woods or thickets with plenty of cover. Some simply perch on any horizontal twig or branch, and many geese, ducks, and swans feel safest in the middle of an expanse of water.

The sleeper carries his bed—his feathers—with him, and he settles down and "puts his head under his wing." In fact what he does is to bury his beak up to the nostrils under his shoulder-feathers (Fig. 6), thus anchoring his long neck. When this is done he may end up like a ball of feathers (Fig. 7).

Herons find it hard to turn their heads round because of the way their necks are jointed; they sleep with the beak to the front, tucked inside one carpal joint. A whole group of otherwise unrelated birds simply draw their heads between their shoulders so that the "chin" is pressed against the neck: this is the sleeping position of bustards, storks (Fig. 8), pigeons, sandgrouse, and many others. The grebe, which sleeps on the water, tucks its beak sideways under its neck (Fig. 9). It is worth noting that penguins and cassowaries, which sleep standing or resting on the tarsus and have diminutive wings, hook the end of the beak behind one wing just as their ancestors with proper wings must have done; while, as already mentioned, a number of birds with well developed wings simply withdraw their heads between their shoulders.

Long-legged birds and those that frequently rest on the ground often sleep on one leg, drawing the other up

FIG. 6.
A European cormorant asleep.

FIG. 8. A black stork asleep.

FIG. 7. A finch asleep.

FIG. 9. A grebe asleep.

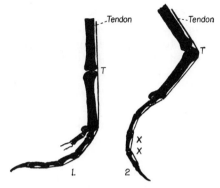

FIG. 10*a*. Diagram of a bird's leg (*1*) with the leg straight, (*2*) with the leg bent as when perching. Since the tendon runs round the outside of the tarsal joint, it curls up the toes to which it is attached, whenever the leg is bent. The locking device acts at the places marked *X*.

FIG. 10*b*. Detail of the locking mechanism at *X* in Fig. 10*a* (much magnified), showing special knobs on the lower surface of the tendon engaged with the special teeth of the tendon sheath. Normally, the tendon slides freely in the sheath, which is attached to the skin of the underside of the toe; but when a bird is on a branch with its toes curled up, its weight presses the teeth against the knobs, which prevents the tendon from slipping.

into the belly-feathers: examples are geese, cranes, storks, and herons. Many people wonder how their canary or a domestic hen manages to sleep on its perch without falling off. It does this with the help of a special device that comes into play as the bird relaxes its leg muscles. When this happens, the tarsal joint is automatically flexed and the toes curl up and grip the perch tighter (Fig. 10*a*). This is helped by an ingenious locking mechanism which prevents the tendon from slipping (Fig. 10*b*).

Woodpeckers and tree creepers rest by hooking themselves in a vertical position on the bark or hollow inside of a tree. I once killed a woodpecker with a well-aimed shot; the bird remained hanging in this position after it was dead. So it is clear that all these queer postures in which birds sleep, although they would be impossible for us, put no strain on a bird's muscles. It is just the same for the long-legged birds that stand on one leg; when the leg is straightened the tarsal joint snaps into place like the blade of a pocketknife, and the leg can only be bent again by a sudden jerk.

If you look at ducks and geese carefully you will notice that when they stand on their left legs, their beaks are hidden under the right shoulder-feathers, and vice versa. Flamingos do just the opposite, turning their beaks to the same side as the leg they stand on (Fig. 11). Unfortunately, artists who paint them usually pay no attention to such subtleties.

While we are on the subject of sleep, let us mention that the only birds that sleep all night and hunt all day are those that find their food mainly by eye—and especially those birds who have relatively small eyes. Large-eyed birds, like the owls and nightjars, are, as everyone knows, mainly nocturnal. To waders and waterfowl the round of day and night is not very important, for with the help of the sensitive organs of touch on their beaks they find their food by groping in mud and slime or

under water. It is a queer experience to hear the many
free-flying ducks in the Berlin Zoo rushing by my window
at literally all hours of the day and night. These birds
sleep just when they feel like it, which means when they
are full and have arranged their feathers—and this can
as well be noon as midnight.

But to return to the nest. Here, too, most people will
immediately think of a songbird's nest, a neat, round
little thing, open on top and probably with a thick and
softly cushioned lining. Many people also think that songbirds usually nest high in the trees. This is true for some
kinds but by no means for all. Most of our small birds
nest in bushes. Then there are the larks and pipits and
some buntings and warblers, which make their nest on
the ground, while those that nest high above the ground
usually breed in holes, where they are protected from
the prying eyes of predatory enemies.

The way the nest is built varies greatly with the species,
from the almost transparent structure of the blackcap to
the finely woven, domed cradles which the long-tailed
tit, the winter wren, and most remarkable of all, the

FIG. 11. Flamingos asleep.

FIG. 12. The nest of the penduline tit. One-fifth natural size.

penduline tit (Fig. 12) build for their young. The tightly woven, felt-like nest of the penduline tit has only a side entrance and hangs from a swaying poplar branch.

These are only a few examples from the passerines. If we take a look at other groups, we will find many new variations. The nightjar, for example, sits on its two eggs on a carpet of pine needles which lie just as they were blown by the wind. The nightjar relies on its remarkable protective coloration and would only advertise its brood if it altered the surroundings by gathering any kind of a nest. The European kingfisher, bee-eater, and bank swallow bore a yard deep into the sandy loam of a cliff and lay their eggs at the end of this tunnel, the kingfisher on fish bones that it throws up, the bank swallow in a warm nest often made of feathers. The grebes gather all sorts of plants under water to make their large floating nests with a shallow hollow on top, in which they lay their eggs. If the water level rises, the eggs lie with their undersides in water.

Everyone will have seen photographs of the huge hundredweight eyries which diurnal raptors, birds of prey such as eagles and hawks, build of thick branches in the tops of trees. Some readers may also have heard of the nesting habits of certain gamebirds, the megapodes of Australia and the neighboring islands. Some kinds of megapodes simply bury their eggs in the sand and leave them to be hatched by the heat of the sun. Others, like the brushturkey, scratch together a gigantic mound of leaves in which the eggs are kept warm by the heat produced as the leaves rot. These piles are always built by the cock, who will not let the hen near his leaf-castle except to mate and lay her eggs (Fig. 13a). He regulates the temperature by scratching leaves on or off the pile, testing the heat with the almost featherless innerside of his wings and with his naked head and neck. But when the young hatch, this anxious father does not concern himself about them in the least. The young are able to fly at once and are so self-reliant that they can make their way in life without ever having met their parents (Fig. 13b). The eggs take from nine to twelve weeks to hatch inside the mound of leaves.

FIG. 13a. A brushturkey cock scratches together a pile of leaves for his mate's eggs to be laid in.

FIG. 13b. A young brushturkey which has just left the egg.

FIG. 14*a*. The nest of a wood duck in a hole. (The owner is shown in Figs. 18 and 88).

FIG. 14*b*. The same covered over with down.

Everybody knows about eiderdown, but few people realize that almost all ducks and geese line their nests with down, which they also use to hide the conspicuously pale eggs on those occasions when they leave the nest to eat, drink, or bathe. Ducks that nest in the open always have gray-brown down, while on those that nest in holes and have no need of protective camouflage for the eggs, it is whitish (Figs. 14*a* and 53).

The actions of nest building are wholly instinctive: they are not learned by practice or imitation, and they begin automatically when the time of egg-laying approaches. A bird who is laying for the first time cannot possibly have any idea of the purpose of the nest it is building, for it cannot know that it is going to lay eggs or have a family to rear. Close observations have shown that, in spite of opinions to the contrary, young birds build nests just as competently as their elders. The stronger the urge to reproduce, the more complete the nest.

Of these elaborate instinctive movements, such as nest building, it seems that no detail is left to the individual's inventiveness to fill in; every member of the species does them the same way. Most birds, for instance, go out and search for material for their nests, but you will never see a duck, a swan, or a goose coming home with nest-stuff in its beak. They simply make a depression in whatever material is at hand, dry grass, leaves, or the rotting wood inside a tree, line it with their own down, and awkwardly gather around such stuff as lies within reach of their beaks. Birds that bring nest-material from a distance fall into two classes: some, like pigeons, herons, and European cormorants, bring back one piece at a time, while others, like the canary, pack their beaks full.

Woodpeckers do not line the deep vertical tunnel they have chiseled out of a tree. We conclude that they have had such nests for many more generations than the hole-nesting passerines such as titmice, European tree and house sparrows, or starlings, which build a fine upholstered nest, more appropriate to an open site, inside the hole.

Young woodpeckers sit in a hard wooden pot, so to speak, and to protect their tender skins from injury the small ones have a kind of callus or heel pad on the tarsal joint (Fig. 15). This heel pad disappears when they are

FIG. 15. A ten-day-old black woodpecker with heel pads on its tarsal joints.

able to sit up and clamber about. If you try to raise young woodpeckers in a flower pot you will find they cannot climb after they have left the nest; their claws have been worn down by the hard surface of the pot, to which evolution has not adapted them. You will have to bring them up in a wooden box if you want them normal. Such experiments show how delicately adjusted a bird is to its natural world and how little we usually know of these adjustments.

As I have mentioned, the different groups of birds have very special, stereotyped ways of building their nests. No woodpecker, for instance, would build its nest out on the fork of a limb. But as often happens when we try to make generalizations, the rules are sometimes unexpectedly broken and we may find two quite different methods of nesting in one group. Of the quite distinct assemblage of birds we call the pigeons or doves, some make open nests in trees and bushes while others look for holes in trees or rocky niches—as does the ancestor of our domestic pigeon, the Mediterranean rock dove (Fig. 51*a*). It is hard to say which sort of nest site was used by the first pigeon ancestors. The glossy, white eggs of all pigeons point to a descent from hole-nesting birds. On the other hand, by far the greatest number of species today—and pigeons are plentiful all over the world—nest in the open. In any case, one parent always stands over the conspicuous clutch of one or two eggs, so that they are not likely to be noticed by a predator. Furthermore all pigeons bring in nest material, though sometimes very little. So we might equally well take the view that the ancestral pigeons were open-nesters.

Most parrots are hole-nesters with woodpecker habits; they simply clean out a pre-existing hole and lay their white eggs on the hard wood. Certain groups of parrots, however, carry in material, and some produce domed nests inside with the entrance above and behind. Parrots do not bring nesting material in the beak or the

FIG. 16. A lovebird hides chips of wood in the feathers of its back to carry them to the nest.

claws, as other birds do, but mainly stick it between the feathers of the back and rump (Fig. 16). The South American quaker parakeet, which some zoos allow to fly free, manages in yet another way: it is a colony nester and makes its homes chiefly in the foundations of the great nests of raptors. Into this jumble of sticks the parakeets bring tiny twigs, and each pair makes its own private home with its own private entrance. When they cannot find such a place, they are almost helpless. They try to pile up twigs on smooth surfaces that will not support them, and the pile either collapses of its own weight or is blown down by a gust of wind.

The big nests of the stork, the osprey, and the sea-eagle also serve as nest sites for small birds such as European tree sparrows and wagtails, which are fond of tangles of wood or twigs. These birds, however, never form nesting colonies like those of the quaker parakeets.

The nesting habits of two kinds of penguins are quite as strange as those of the megapodes mentioned before. The smaller sorts of penguins usually lay their one or two eggs in crannies in the rock or in open hollows, making few changes in the natural site, and incubate their eggs lying down. This is, of course, impossible for the two biggest penguins, the king and the emperor, which nest on or close to the eternal antarctic ice. They rest their single egg on the top of their feet, sheltering it behind a special fold of belly-skin which is developed in both sexes (Fig. 17). When the mate comes back from fishing, the pair approach breast to breast until their toes touch; the penguin who has been guarding the egg rolls it with his beak onto the feet of the other bird, so that the egg never touches the ice. The young, which are at first quite helpless and dependent on their parents for food, are treated in the same way as the eggs: they live like little marsupials. Now that there are many king penguins in zoos, this singular manner of brooding has been repeatedly observed and photographed.

The males of some birds weave beautifully delicate nests which serve as an advertisement to woo any female considering marriage. The female weaver bird or penduline tit does not show up until the male has almost finished his work of art (Fig. 12). Perhaps it is the sight of the dwelling which puts her in the right frame of mind. Something of the same kind also happens among the woodpeckers; at any rate, the male black or spotted

FIG. 17. An incubating king penguin. The egg is carried resting on the feet in a pouch of the skin.

woodpecker is the master carpenter of the nesting hole, and, in addition, he later takes an active part in hatching the eggs.

The male weaver bird and penduline tit seem to desert at least the first nest of the season as soon as the female has laid her eggs and started incubation. The male then builds another nest, waits again for a wife, and after setting her up may even go on to a third nest. When the busy architect finally tires of building, he settles down and helps raise the last brood.

In many species, such as storks, gulls, and eagles, both parents bring nest material. In some, like European black-birds and finches, the female alone builds the nest, while in others the male brings the material and his wife makes the nest. A bachelor black-crowned night heron seeks out a thick or forked branch and carries up to it all sorts of twigs and bits of branches, but he leaves them scattered around his perch so that they either fall off or form the beginnings of several different nests. When a lovesick female shows up, he hands her nest material, to the accompaniment of special sounds and postures of greeting. The female arranges the stuff around herself and thus becomes the center of the nest as it grows.

In the spring the unmated cock pigeon looks for a nesting place, which, depending on his species, may be a hole or a forked limb. Here he sits, calling tirelessly in a special voice to attract females. When he succeeds, his first reaction may be to drive the female away, just as the gray heron does, because he is not yet used to such close bodily contact with members of his own species. He may throw her out several times more before the two finally accept each other and start building or otherwise protesting their affection with gestures and sounds. The male gray heron and pigeon are thus clearly unaware that having a nest and starting a family means putting up with a wife as well. Once mated, however, these birds remain faithful to one another and also recog-

FIG. 18. A pair of wood ducks looking for a nest. The drake hangs like a woodpecker at the entrance of the hole, inspecting his future nesting place. About one-eighth natural size.

nize each other when they meet away from the nest.

Unlike the gray heron, the cock pigeon never starts bringing nest material until he is properly paired, and even then some time passes before the nest-building drive awakens. So when you see a wood pigeon flying with a twig in his beak, you can be sure that he has found not only a nesting place but a wife to give his twig to.

We are far from knowing how much these observations apply to all those birds which nest in pairs and are thus, so to speak, married, for there are still too few thorough studies following marked animals.

Even when a male takes no part in tending the eggs or young, he often selects the nesting place, or he and his wife choose it together. This is true of many ducks and gallinaceous birds. A domestic cock will crawl into the hen-house and cluck officiously, pointing out to his hens the allotted corner to lay their eggs in. I have seen much the same thing in eider ducks, pintail, mallard, and wood ducks (Fig. 18). On subsequent days the drake again accompanies his wife when she goes to lay her eggs. But when the clutch is complete and she settles to incubate properly, he goes back to his male friends and forgets all about affairs of love, all the more because he now puts on his dull summer dress and for some weeks cannot fly.

Closely related species often do things very differently. In geese and swans, as well as a few other waterfowl, the male shares the incubation of the eggs. In certain tree-ducks the male even hatches the eggs and raises the young by himself. In the white swans of the Old and New Worlds the males do not seem to take part in incubation, but they may now and then stand over the eggs to guard them (Fig. 19). On the other hand, the Australian black swan, like the male pigeon, takes his regular turn on the eggs from morning to afternoon and is then relieved by the female.

FIG. 19.
A male mute swan guarding his nest.

FIG. 20. Nightjars change place in the nest.

One must not think that birds regard incubation as a tedious duty and are glad when the mate comes at the end of a spell and they can leave the nest. In many species the opposite is true: the bird coming to relieve its mate may often have to shove the sitting bird gently off the eggs (Fig. 20).

Certain birds have regular hours or regular intervals for changing over at the nest. These intervals vary greatly. Some small birds spend only ten or twenty minutes on the nest at a time, while vultures stay there two or three days and the emperor penguin as long as fifteen. It depends of course on how much food the bird needs and where and how it gets it.

Some parent birds that do not normally take turns on the nest will nevertheless cover the eggs in an emergency. The male California quail, for instance, guards the nest and the female but does not usually sit on the eggs. But if the hen dies and he sees the nest unattended, he promptly goes to it and sits on the eggs; when the young hatch, he leads them about like a proper mother.

The opposite can happen too: birds that have a very regular shift-system will not interrupt it even in emergencies. Among the cockatiels, for instance, the eggs are incubated during the day by the cock and at night by the hen. Even if the female falls sick and dies and the eggs become chilled, the male would never think of leaving his roosting place at the entrance of the nest-hole to go in and sit on them during the night. And so the eggs die.

In some species the length of time the pair will incubate is instinctive. If after the prescribed period nothing has hatched out, the eggs are left. Some pigeons faithfully take turns at incubating but will desert the eggs if they have not hatched in a fixed number of days: 13 for the passenger pigeon, 17 for the domestic pigeon. These birds will leave their eggs even when the squabs are already breaking out of the shell and peeping; you can prove this by removing the eggs of a pair of nesting pigeons and putting them back a day later so that the young hatch 24 hours late.

Some domestic pigeons, however, behave very differently, having lost, through domestication, the finer shades of their instinctive behavior. They may even sit on their eggs too long. The same is true of domestic geese and domestic ducks. We do not know much about how this is in wild birds; but some, like the lapwing, seem regularly to go on incubating their eggs if they do not hatch at the right time—for instance, if they have been killed by frost.

People are always asking whether hens lay if there is no cock about. The answer is yes, for the act of laying corresponds not to the birth of a mammal but rather to the periods of heat which recur regularly if a female is not fertilized. In a wild bird the time of egg-laying is affected by the male, whose courtship starts the egg developing; also young farmyard hens start laying earlier when there is a rooster around.

You see this too with birds that have abnormal fixations. A tame female pigeon or parrot may be so excited by her human keeper's caresses that she lays an infertile egg. If there are no males around, captive females will sometimes pair and behave sexually to one another. And two males can form a pair in the same way.

What happens if you take away the eggs a bird has

just laid? The answer varies with the species. Some birds finish laying the usual number of eggs; if the whole clutch is taken away, the pair will rapidly revert to courtship and often build a new nest before laying again. This is what happens in pigeons. Other species seem to have a feeling that there ought to be a certain number of eggs in the clutch and just go on laying if you remove one egg every day. A yellow-shafted flicker was once tricked in this way into laying 71 eggs in 73 days, and a green woodpecker got up to 17. Such birds can go on laying indefinitely to the point of exhaustion.

Some domestic hens and ducks have been bred to lay eggs but not to incubate. The hatching is then the work of an incubator or of a hen that is not just an egg-laying machine.

Not every bird will lay again after its eggs have been removed. Birds that habitually have several broods during the spring and summer keep going as long as their sex glands keep working, which means until they begin to molt. Many large vultures and eagles do not lay again if their one and only egg is taken; they have no natural enemies and are not adapted for such an emergency.

3. *The Brood*

There is an old custom that the farmer's wife picks out eggs which are new laid or not yet incubated and sets them under a hen just as the clock strikes twelve on a Sunday. As a result, all the chicks hatch out together, in about twenty days.

How does a wild bird regulate the order in which its eggs will hatch out? Some large birds such as owls, whose young stay in the nest after they are hatched, begin incubating as soon as the first egg is laid and then add another egg every day or two. The young hatch at the same intervals and vary greatly in size. In Figure 21 you see three Ural owls hatched in the same nest. The youngest is eight days old, the next ten, and the eldest eleven.

This difference in size is especially pronounced in the downy nestlings of the short-eared owl. The nest stands in the open in a bog and from a distance it looks like a tall white molehill. At the top is the head of the biggest youngster; tightly clustered around it are all its brothers and sisters, each smaller than the last, so that the individuals merge in a mass of downy white owlet.

Pigeons lay their first egg in the late afternoon, and the parents take turns standing over it without really sitting, so that while it is hidden from view and does not get cold, it is not properly incubated. When the next egg comes two days later, the real incubation begins

FIG. 21. Three Ural owls of the same brood.

and both nestlings hatch at just about the same time, in 16½ days.

Many songbirds, birds of prey, and others whose young remain for some time in the nest start to incubate after laying has started but before it is completed. As a result, part of the clutch hatches together and the rest a little later.

Birds such as grebes and rails, whose young leave the nest soon after hatching, sometimes start to incubate before the clutch is complete. They then have the problem of taking care of eggs and young at the same time. When incubation is the care of both parents, the one who is off the nest looks after the young. But things can get difficult when there is only one adult to tend a large brood. It is then essential that the young hatch out all together; for when they are a few hours old, they leave the nest and are conducted by the old bird to a suitable place to feed or rest.

It is extraordinary how a female black grouse or mallard, both of which have to manage everything by themselves, lays and broods her eggs. The first egg is usually laid in moist ground and then covered with grass. Every day the mother comes back and lays another egg, each time sitting a little longer on the nest, until with the final egg the true incubation begins. If you mark the eggs and hold them up to the light when the last is laid, you will find that the first egg—which was warmed whenever the mother came back to lay—has already started to develop. It may be that the eggs that the mother carries around inside her and lays last develop slightly during this time and so need less incubation then the others. At any rate, if all goes well the eleven to thirteen eggs of the mallard all hatch out, after twenty-six days, within about two hours of each other. The ducklings dry themselves under the mother and then rub against her to get oil on their down; within a few hours they have made themselves watertight and can be led out of the nest.

One gets the impression that the youngsters do not need any urging. They are so impatient to be away that their mother has only to show them the road. Instinct tells her that ducklings cannot fly but make their way by running, jumping, and swimming; when she sets off along the familiar route to the water she walks instead of flying. If one of the children lags behind, it peeps shrilly, and the mother waits for it to catch up or comes back to it; this slow, halting pilgrimage to the water often cover hundreds of yards.

Events that are not provided for in the duck's instincts usually end in tragedy, for birds are generally not bright enough to cope with situations that have to be thought out. If mallards cannot find cover on the ground to nest in, they may choose a hollow tree or an old raptor's nest; when the time comes for the young to leave, they simply tumble down. Then the whole family forms up at the foot of the tree and sets off for the nearest water. In nature these feeble little balls of down are almost never hurt, when they fall, but in a big city there may be trouble. A mallard once built her nest in the middle of Berlin, on the flat roof of a four-story house where the city's Institute for Nature Protection had its office. The tiny ducklings jumped off the roof and pitched onto the hard street below, where most of them were killed. Passersby were horrified, and some of them reported the incident to the Institute.

FIG. 22. Wood duck babies, only a few hours old, before their 30-foot jump from their nest to the ground. About one-eighth natural size.

The following year, when the duck came back and laid her eggs in the same place, I was called in. I had a low fence built around the nest and examined the eggs to see when they would hatch. On the appropriate day we were warned by telephone that the young were emerging and armed ourselves with a big net in which we caught the mother as she was leaving the nest; the ducklings were of course stopped by the little fence. We put them all in a box and took them to a pond in the zoo three miles away. At the edge of the pond we quietly opened the door of the box, so as not to frighten the mother, and after a little time she and her brood swam out. The next year the duck, whom we had ringed, picked out the same nesting site again, and the whole show took place once more.

Another duck story: Years ago I set up in the Berlin Zoo some logs with smooth holes in them (Figs. 18 and 22) as nest sites for the wood ducks and mandarin ducks which were allowed to fly around loose. The newly hatched ducklings could clamber up to the mouth of the cavity and jump down to the ground almost 30 feet below (Fig. 22). But when we looked at these nests in the autumn, we found the mummified remains of several mallard ducklings. Mallards had nested in the holes, and mallard ducklings do not have the equipment to get out of holes like these. The young of ducks that usually breed in holes—wood ducks, mandarin ducks, golden-eyes, and muscovy ducks—have sharp claws with which they can clamber up steep, smooth surfaces. If you put them in a deep box covered with wire netting, they will climb up and run along the netting upside down; nature gives them this means of climbing out of the nest holes, and gravity takes care of the journey to the ground. But it is totally different for the offspring of ducks that usually nest on the ground. If the young cannot get out of a deep hole, the nesting hole or any other, the mother hasn't the sense to lift her children with her beak or to squat down and let them use her as a ladder. If on the way to the water a duckling falls into a hole it cannot get out of, its mother makes no attempt to help it. She waits around for a while listening to its cries of distress; but if it cannot manage by itself, she finally goes off with its more fortunate brothers and sisters and leaves it to die.

4. *More about Nesting*

If you drive a pair of birds away from their nest or disturb the eggs, will they desert the nest for good? This depends on what you did and what kind of bird it is. If you simply touch the eggs, no bird will ever notice it unless you have upset the owner as well or have greatly disturbed the surroundings of the nest.

I have noticed that birds which begin nesting early in the spring and have three or four broods are more likely to desert the first lot than the last. In the spring the sex glands are so swollen that the birds are more likely to breed again than in summer when they only wish to brood and feed their young.

Apart from this, a bird's readiness to desert its nest depends both on its species and on how it is disturbed. If I want to examine the eggs of a mallard nesting in the open without frightening her away for good, I approach the nest openly so that the mother can see me when I am still some way off and will not think that I am stalking her. As I come nearer, the duck instinctively crouches, waiting to see whether I notice her; when I get too close, she flies away. I examine the eggs to see how long they have been incubated, then put them back, covering them with down again, and go away. The mother will meanwhile have found a pond where she will preen, drink, or feed, and then will make her way back to the nest as if nothing unusual had happened.

If I want to scare the mother mallard away so that a rarer species may use the nest site, all I have to do is to creep up and make a grab at her. She flies away uttering alarm cries and is not so likely to come back, for she now connects the nest with danger to her life.

The same is true of the wood pigeons of Europe, and the idea that they easily desert their nests is wrong in the case of the pairs that live in cities. If I come upon a nest in a wood little frequented by man, the brooding bird crashes off in terror and does not return. But in the Berlin Zoo I have often climbed a ladder to examine a wood pigeon's nest; sometimes the bird jumps out and flutters along the ground, pretending to have a broken wing, or it gets up unwillingly and perches on the nearest branch until I go away. Either way the bird quickly resumes incubating. These park birds are so used to the sight of people that they treat them as much smaller predators or ignore them.

On the whole, a bird that is incubating eggs or brooding small young will always return unless it has been made to fear for its life. I do not know how people got the idea that birds know when their eggs have been handled, because most birds can smell very little. Maybe people used to tell this to their children to keep them from bothering the nests.

We mentioned the "broken-wing trick" of the wood pigeon. You may have seen the same thing happen; as you approach a bush, a European white-throat (Old World warbler of the genus *Sylvia*) drops to the ground and flutters about in the grass, apparently helpless. This means that you are close to the nest or to the young which have recently left it. The broken-wing trick draws predators away from the brood. Since it occurs in the most diverse families—partridges, ducks, plovers (Fig. 23), and cranes—we wonder whether the behavior evolved separately in each group or was characteristic of the ancestors of most birds and was later lost by some of them. All we can say is that the birds which feign injury in that way are most often those that nest on or

FIG. 23. The broken-wing trick. A ringed plover has caught sight of a crow not far from its nest.

close to the ground; a crow looking for food in the tree tops would not pay much attention to something fluttering on the ground below.

The layman probably thinks that this trick is done consciously—that the bird really knows that a fox can be deceived in this way. This is certainly not so; every member of the species acts in the same manner in the face of the same danger, and you can hardly suppose that a bird which is breeding for the first time spends its time working out what to do if an enemy comes along. The whole business must be inborn.

For a time it was thought that a bird became so stiff while sitting on its eggs that it could not walk properly when it left the nest. But there is no question of this. A duck that has been swimming about actively with her young, or up-ending for food, tries the same trick as the European white-throat.

An experiment with mallards that live in parks and have grown used to people shows the exact circumstances when the trick is used. If you walk up to a mallard mother who is brooding her family or herding them on the edge of a pond, she first lets out a gentle warning cry, with head raised, and then swims quickly off with her children. But if you noisily row up to the family on the water, looking straight at them, the mother sounds the alarm, the ducklings scatter in all directions and dive, and the frightened parent threshes around on the water as if she were badly hurt and could not get away.

Every now and then one finds nests built in some absurd place like the middle of a busy road. These nests are usually deserted as soon as incubation starts. From my own observations I would say that this happens because the birds select the site, build the nest, and lay their eggs early in the mornings when almost nobody is about. It does not say much for their brains that a pair of birds which have lived several years in the same place and must know that at certain times a road is always crowded go ahead and build their nest there.

The uninitiated have no idea how many parasites there are in the nests of small birds. These parasites weaken and sometimes actually kill the helpless nestlings. If you notice that a pair of wagtails are not flying to and from their nest as eagerly as they were, and that the young birds are calling persistently but more and more feebly, take a look at the nest. The youngsters, which are almost ready to fly, may seem perfectly all right, though a little inactive, until you take them out and look at their bellies. You will then see that the naked skin is covered with little red spots, and in the bottom of the nest you will find as many as 120 little maggots, the larvae of a dirty blue-gray fly called *Lucilia sordida*.

Later broods seem to suffer most from these attacks, for the number of egg-laying flies increases as the season advances. Unless we help them, these heavily infested nestlings are condemned to die. The simplest remedy is to make a new nest out of dry grass in the same place and put the chicks in it. The parents will go on feeding,

FIG. 24. Five nests a European blackbird started building between the rungs of a ladder.

and by the time the young leave the nest they will have recovered.

The nests of barn swallows and hole-nesting birds often swarm with lice, fleas, and wingless flies; the young birds may suffer slow death or deformity from the bites, or the growth of their feathers may be affected so that the wings are useless. It is all the more surprising that birds like wagtails, which are such skilled catchers of insects, should allow their young to be eaten alive instead of feeding on the parasites.

Everything considered, a bird's nest is not such a sweet and pleasant place as most people think. We may even say that the times at the nest are for the old birds and even more for the young the most dangerous periods of their lives. Quite aside from starvation and natural enemies of all sorts, they are at the mercy of rainstorms, hail, and even floods. Of the broods started by European blackbirds and song thrushes, more than half are total losses.

Birds that do not breed in colonies often make serious mistakes when building their nests. If a pair of European redstarts is building in a niche of ornamental stonework where there are several sites close together, they often carry material first to one niche and then to another, finally becoming so confused that they give up.

A European blackbird once elected to build in a garden where three ladders hung together on a wall (Fig.

24). The angle between a rung and one of the long supports was a fine site to build in, but unfortunately there were a dozen or more such sites, each very like the others. The bird began to build in nine places but finally gave up without completing any of its nests. European redstarts that begin several nests in similar sites may manage to complete two or three of them; the nest the first egg is laid in becomes the real nest, and there is no more confusion afterwards.

Domestic pigeons, which live in colonies, have the same trouble but with more serious results. On returning to the dovecote a pigeon may by mistake enter the box above or below its own. Then there is a pitched battle, heads are bloodied, and the young are trampled underfoot as the rightful owner attacks the trespasser, who is still under the impression that he is in his own home and that it has been invaded by a stranger. If man were not gifted with language, he would probably have the same trouble with hotel rooms.

5. *Can a Bird Recognize Its Own Eggs?*

There is no general answer to this question. Experiments show that a great many birds—among them raptors, gamebirds, and waterfowl—not only do not distinguish their own eggs from others of their own species but will try to incubate anything they can manage to sit on. Color and shape seem of little importance; swans have been seen incubating bottles, and I have gotten broody pigeons, which lay white eggs, to incubate the bright, boldly spotted eggs of plovers. Some birds, however, are upset if the change is too great. Experiments on gulls and terns, whose eggs are greenish or brownish with darker blotches, showed that these birds frequently refused to accept eggs that were painted a glaring red. These birds sometimes objected to white eggs too, but we must add that an egg may at first be refused or avoided and later accepted: it depends a lot on how broody the bird is.

Small birds which have to put up with European cuckoos may be more discriminating; they will be discussed in Chapter 10.

Everybody knows that a great many birds eat eggs and feed their own young on the very nourishing contents. The crow family and the gulls come first to mind. The question is: why don't these birds eat their own eggs? Ornithologists have now shown that crows or gulls consider their own nest taboo and will protect anything in it as long as it looks something like an egg or a young bird. But if you move the egg of a herring gull a yard or two from the nest, the parents will gobble it up, just as they eat the eggs other herring gulls have left unprotected. What is more, you can pack a gull's nest full of extra eggs and he or his mate will sit on top of the pile without harming them.

6. Can a Bird Recognize Its Own Young?

This depends on whether or not the young leave the nest soon after hatching. If you put a duck egg or a hen's egg in place of the egg of a female eagle or Old World kite which is kept by herself, she will brood it without any fuss. When the chick emerges she tries to feed it; if the young bird instinctively runs out of the nest, she treats it as a prey instead of something to be nourished: she catches and eats it.

I have often put different kinds of eggs under nesting hens and found that whether the foster mother will leave the nest with the newly hatched chicks or kill them depends partly on her breed; there are also individual differences. By no means every hen will raise ducklings she has hatched out. Some will not accept pheasant chicks, which are closely related to chickens, and there are even hens which will accept only chicks whose down is colored like that of the South Asiatic red jungle-fowl, the wild ancestor of our domestic chickens.

Very few domestic hens can be expected to mother species whose young stay in the nest and are fed by their parents, for these young birds behave very differently from the hen's own chicks. I once gave a raven's egg to a bantam to incubate and forgot to go to the nest before dawn on the day the egg was to hatch. By the time I got there the young raven was dead. After this I took care to move strange eggs to the incubator before the nestlings announced their imminent arrival by peeping and pecking at the shell.

The hatchling's voice, as well as its looks, may arouse the foster mother's hostility—as another unhappy experience taught me. I had a hen which devotedly incubated a bustard's egg although it was very different in color and size from her own. As the young bustard was boring its way out through the shell, instead of whispering like a gamebird it uttered the typical long, drawn-out, shrill peep of a bustard, and the hen pecked it to death through the shell.

Among the domestic fowl the instincts of breeds such as gamecock and phoenix, which are similar to the wild ancestor, are not so mixed up as those of the large Asiatic brahmas and cochins. You could set brahmas and cochins on a potato and they would hatch it out!

Parents whose young leave the nest early seem to know without experience how their own young should look and sound. If the young are not the way the parent thinks they ought to be, they are either ignored or treated as enemies and killed. I had experience of this with a wild mallard nesting on an island. I had given her some wood ducks' eggs in place of her own, hoping to raise a breeding colony of wood ducks. On the day of hatching I looked through my field glasses and saw the mallard sitting on the nest while the peeping wood-ducklings swam around on the water. On closer examination I found that the mother was sitting on the empty eggshells, evidently waiting for some young mallards to hatch. To the young wood ducks, which look slightly different from her own kind of ducklings, she paid no attention: evidently they were not the right stimulus to make her leave the nest and swim off with them.

A friend of mine who knows a great deal about these matters once put a couple of ring-necked pheasant's eggs under a hen golden pheasant incubating her own clutch. All the chicks hatched on the same day; and when little heads appeared under her breast feathers, the bird brooded them like a true loving mother pheasant. But suddenly her eye fell on a small head that did not look right—one of the ring-necked pheasants. She gave a start and prepared to peck it, but her mother-love surged up again for this little creature which was, after all, not so very different from her own young. Broodiness and hostility alternated for a little time before she finally accepted the stranger.

Birds whose young stay in the nest for some time after hatching will raise the young of other species along with their own. It is easy to get a European blackbird to hatch the eggs of a song thrush and feed the young; and the same is true of the European sparrowhawk and European buzzard (a hawk of the genus *Buteo*), and probably of many other birds.

Most young birds who leave the nest early learn in the first few days to tell their parents from other adults and also to recognize each other. A mallard mother soon comes to tell her own young from those of other mallards: if the family encounter a strange mallard duckling, they set on it and sometimes even kill it. On the other hand, a pair of European blackbirds will feed a young stranger of their species that happens to wander into the area where their own family is dispersed.

Domestic pigeons will feed young pigeons from other nests if you exchange them early and if the nestlings are not too different in age. One reason for this may be that it is usually rather dark in a dovecote, so that for a time after hatching the parents hardly know what their offspring look like and just pump their crop-milk into any young bird that inserts its beak into their throats. Young pigeons that are old enough to fly but are not yet self-supporting often go begging to their neighbors; they are pecked away by the females, but every now and then a male that is about to feed its own young will feed them.

The urge to get food and give it to someone usually comes over adult birds, especially males, around hatching time. We can see this in solitary male song thrushes or European robins which are kept in cages. These birds are usually greedy for mealworms; but after the spring period of song is over, they will take a worm from you and kill it, but instead of eating it will hop around nervously, making their characteristic nesting calls. They even try to give it back to you or push it into a crevice. Yet they cannot know what they are trying to do, because they have never had young to feed.

Another example of this unreasoning urge. A tame jackdaw was given the care of a young rook which was not yet able to feed itself and which begged for food with gaping beak. Soon the jackdaw went to the food dish and stuffed its young companion's mouth full of meat, repeating this action whenever the youngster gaped. The step-child prospered and became independent and started getting food for itself. But now the jackdaw jealously defended the food, attacking the rook whenever it tried to eat. The jackdaw had fed the youngster to satisfy its own feeding urge and not for any reasons of compassion.

7. Who Looks After the Young?

As usual, the answer to this question is that it varies. Some parents, like the megapodes (Fig. 13*a*), do not concern themselves at all with their brood. Many other species come into the world almost as fully developed as the megapodes; their parents lead them to suitable feeding grounds and protect them, but leave them to get their own food from the beginning. Most ducks and geese are like this. If you take the eggs of a goldeneye from its nest hole, hatch them at home, and put the ducklings into a bathtub of water as soon as they are dry, they will dive and search about on the bottom and will snap up any mealworms you have dropped in. The mother duck never thinks of feeding her young, and of course the father is not there. Unfortunately, the sentimental public—including most newspaper reporters—call such behavior unmotherly and unloving. Mother ducks do not feed their offspring because they do not have the instinct, as the ducklings can do it all for themselves within a few hours of hatching.

The parents of many species—gamebirds, cranes, bustards, and rails—pick up a grasshopper or a beetle and offer it to one of the chicks, but this happens only until the young are a few days old; after this time the young can distinguish for themselves what is good to eat. In cranes and rails both parents give food to the young, but

FIG. 25. A male emu looking after his young.

among domestic chickens usually only the mother does.

We have seen that species whose young leave the nest early sometimes live in pairs, sometimes separated. The rearing of the children may thus be a job for both parents, for the mother alone, or, as in emus (Fig. 25), for the father. If the young remain in the nest for a time, monogamy is nearly always the rule; since the young cannot get their own food, looking after them is a job for two. The father and mother may take turns, one flying out for food while the other feeds the young; in the extreme case of certain raptors, the female stays at the nest from the time the first egg is laid until the young leave the nest, so that for weeks on end the male must bring food for her and for the young.

Between these extremes there are all sorts of intermediates. If you watch a European blackbird's nest you will notice that the female does almost all the incubation of the eggs and brooding of the young, but that in some way the father knows when the children have hatched; he then starts flying to and fro bringing beakfuls of worms which he hands over to his wife (Fig. 26) and she puts into the gaping throats of her family. When the young get a little bigger, the cock also takes part in giving them food; after a little more than a week the offspring, which are now well feathered, are left uncovered while both parents gather food.

Many thrushes and woodpeckers are not particularly fond of their mates, and each parent has its own hunting area. The result is that the mates hardly meet at all during this time; at the nest one parent waits on a neighboring twig while the other is feeding the young, or flies off if it sees its mate coming. But this is by no means true of all small birds. A pair of linnets will fly off together to the open field, fill their crops, and come back at the same time to feed their gaping nestlings.

Raptors have a fairly complete division of labor when caring for their young. This is perhaps most marked in European sparrowhawks, which have been the subject of intensive studies. The male is only about half the weight of the female (Fig. 27); from this fact you could guess that they will go about raising their young differently from vultures, European cormorants, and storks, in which the male and female are much the same size. From the time she begins building the nest the hen European sparrowhawk stops hunting and spends all her time at the nest; when the eggs are laid she incubates them con-

FIG. 26. A male European blackbird brings his mate pieces of worm to feed to the nestlings.

a. Male

FIG. 27. European sparrowhawks. One-fifth natural size.

b. Female

tinuously. Her small mate probably would not be large
enough to cover the eggs if he tried.

Soon after incubation begins, the female European
sparrowhawk starts to molt her wing- and tail-feathers, for
she has little need to fly at this time. The male delays his
molt until the breeding season is over; in the meantime he
is busy hunting the elusive little birds his wife and family
need for food. This is his job for two months, one month
until the four or five eggs hatch and another until the
young fly. When he returns from the hunt, the male
either calls the female to meet him and take the prey
in the air or throws it to her on the nest. Since young
raptors cannot cope with a dead bird whole, the mother
tears off small pieces of meat and offers them to the
nestlings. (Vultures are an exception; they feed their

chicks from the crop.) As the children get their feathers, they gradually become better and better at pulling the food to bits by themselves. The father does not know about shredding the food for his children; as a result, if the female dies the fluffy little European sparrow-hawks usually starve to death amid a heap of food their father has brought them. In addition, the unprotected nestlings quickly die of cold or wet if the weather turns bad.

Although the male usually shows no inclination to tear up food for the young, he has been known to do it. Once the mother of a brood of week-old European sparrowhawks was shot and the young seemed destined to die. Their father brought food in plenty but the chicks could not deal with it. Then a lucky thing happened: it did not rain for two days and nights and the weather stayed warm. During these two days the feeding instinct of the male had time to awaken and he began shredding bits of meat and stuffing them into the throats of his children, which, by this time, had become so weak they could hardly stand up. The nestlings quickly recovered and were successfully reared.

The way this European sparrowhawk acted recalls the behavior of the male California quail mentioned earlier, who, although he does not usually brood, took the place of his hen when she died. As we shall see later, a similar kind of substitution sometimes occurs in sexual behavior.

8. *Do Large Birds Take Longer To Hatch Their Eggs?*

Some groups of birds have very long incubation periods in spite of their small size, and vice versa. But within a group the smaller species generally hatch their eggs more quickly than the larger. The eggs of a large species of parrot need about a month to hatch, while those of a small one take only about 18 days. The same holds for the raptors: the biggest vultures incubate seven or eight weeks, the smallest falcons only four. On the other hand, the incubation period of the biggest species of goose, weighing about 9 pounds, is 28 days, exactly the same as that of the smallest, the Australian maned goose, which weighs only a quarter as much.

The incubation period also depends partly on how well developed the birds must be when they leave the egg. The shortest brooders are the small songbirds, whose eggs hatch in a week and a half into blind, naked, helpless nestlings which cannot leave the nest for some time. Two of the longest incubation periods are those of the emu and cassowary, each nearly eight weeks. When these eggs hatch out, the chicks are covered with down and are able at once to run after their father, who tends them.

All this seems very reasonable, but there are extraordinary exceptions. All petrels—from the 18-pound albatross to the little black storm-petrel which weighs less than 2 ounces and is no bigger than a swift—lay one single egg, which the large species brood for about nine weeks and the smallest more than five weeks. This small petrel's egg weighs about a quarter of an ounce, but it takes nearly the same length of time to hatch as the egg of the rhea, the 45-pound South American ostrich-like bird, whose egg is more than 80 times as heavy. From the petrel's egg there creeps out a feeble creature whose

FIG. 28*a*. The young European nuthatch, which grows up in the safety of a hole in a tree, is still helpless at 13 days. (Adult weight three-fourths ounce.) One half natural size.

FIG. 28*b*. The young European blackbird grows up exposed to all sorts of dangers in an open nest, which it is ready to leave at 13 days. (Adult weight 3½ ounces.) One half natural size.

parents will have to feed it for many weeks, while the rhea's egg produces a nimble chick which is ready to explore the world.

Among these confusing facts I would like to mention certain adaptations which have been brought about by natural selection. Very long incubation periods, which usually go with slow development after hatching, may be regarded as characteristic of the ancestors of modern birds. Nowadays birds which have developed in this way nest where they are protected from enemies (and perhaps also from bad weather)—in holes or on islands. Among birds whose broods are exposed to all sorts of dangers, the time spent in the egg and in the nest until the bird can fly must be cut as short as possible; the young bird develops the full use of its senses and limbs very early (compare Figs. 28a and b). This is the only way we can explain why the African ostrich, which breeds in a land swarming with hungry predators, sits on its 3-pound egg only six weeks, while the much smaller emu and cassowary, living in Australia where there are fewer predators, incubate their eggs, which are less than half the weight, for eight weeks.

9. *Is the Size of a Bird Related to the Size of Its Egg?*

We can say in general that a large bird lays eggs which are smaller for its weight than those of a small bird. The ostrich weighs sixty times as much as her egg, an average domestic hen twenty-five times as much, and a little hummingbird only eight times as much as hers. People are amazed when they first hear that an ostrich egg is as big as twenty-five hen eggs, but they forget that an ostrich weighs far more than twenty-five hens.

The number of eggs in the full clutch often affects their size. A 13-ounce partridge lays fifteen eggs or more, each about one-thirtieth of her weight, so that altogether they amount to half her weight. This seems reasonable enough, but we would be wrong if we concluded that this is always the case. A mandarin duck, weighing a pound, sometimes produces a clutch of thirteen eggs as big as hen eggs, laying them in as many days; together they weigh one-fifth as much again as she does. In this species the egg weight and clutch size do not seem to be adjusted to each other. Just as remarkable is the common sandpiper, which only weighs 1½ ounces and yet on successive days lays four eggs whose total weight is more than her own. Her relatives, the smaller snipes and plovers, do much the same.

A kiwi weighs about 4½ pounds and her single egg about a fifth as much. The short-toed eagle, which is the same size, lays a single egg which is only one-fourteenth of the mother's weight. The eaglet when it hatches is relatively undeveloped in comparison with the kiwi, and it remains for a comparatively long time dependent on its parents in the nest.

But it is not true to say that the eggs are always relatively small in species whose young hatch in an undeveloped state. Both the fulmar and the much heavier raven come into the world as helpless young, but the adults weigh respectively seven and forty times as much as their eggs.

We shall see in the next chapter how the common or European cuckoo adjusts the size of its eggs to the birds which are going to hatch them.

10. *Cuckoos and the Like*

The European cuckoo has become famous for getting other birds to hatch its eggs. The European cuckoo weighs as much as a blackbird, about 4 ounces, but it lays an egg weighing only half as much as the blackbird's quarter-ounce egg. Indeed, the European cuckoo's egg is as tiny as the egg of the 1 ounce house sparrow.

The egg hatches after 12¼ days, usually quicker than its nest-mates, so that the young European cuckoo emerges at least as early as they do. The European cuckoo has adapted its whole method of breeding to suit itself to the small songbirds that eat the same kind of insect food. The hen European cuckoo sits around watching suitable small birds build their nests and never tries to lay her own egg until she finds a new nest, of the right species, in which the owner has not finished laying. It is very important that the hosts be at the right stage. If the European cuckoo's egg were laid among a clutch that had already been incubated, the young that belonged there would hatch first and the European cuckoo might not be able to push them out of the nest—it might even be trampled to death by them. To lay the egg too early in the host's nest would be equally disastrous.

The hen European cuckoo gets her egg into the foster parent's nest either by laying it there directly or by pushing it in with her beak. Afterwards she regularly removes one of the eggs of the host.

In general the ground color and spotting of the European cuckoo's egg correspond closely to the eggs of its host; there is even a pure blue type that is found with the eggs of the European redstart, which are a similar color. With the notable exception of the hedge sparrow, the color of a European cuckoo's egg never differs much from the color of those of a bird which accepts it. Where there is only one host species, the resemblance may be remarkable: for instance, in northern Sweden, where the European cuckoo almost always uses the brambling, and in Finland, where it usually picks on the European redstart.

In Germany, where the European cuckoo imposes on a great variety of hosts, the eggs vary greatly in appearance. For some foster species, such as the wren, certain warblers, and the hedge sparrow, the color of the eggs is evidently not adapted at all. This apparently happens because, at least in the first two, the host's beak is not strong enough to evict the strange egg from the deep nest.

Experiments have been made with certain warblers and shrikes, who are among the European cuckoo's favorite foster parents, to see just how readily these birds will accept strange eggs. It was found that if the eggs were different enough the birds noticed it, but that they were far less discriminating than a man. If the appearance of the clutch has been greatly changed, almost any small bird will throw out a strange egg or desert the nest.

It also turns out that songbirds do not know their own eggs. An observer took a garden warbler's eggs out of her nest and put in their place the eggs of a lesser whitethroat. The warbler came back, laid another egg, and taking one look at the mixed group threw out the egg she had just laid and incubated the rest. Because her own egg stood out from the others in size and color she obviously thought it was wrong.

Certain birds that would seem to be suitable foster parents almost never harbor European cuckoos' eggs. Perhaps hen European cuckoos occasionally try them out, but the eggs are not accepted. I myself once put a European cuckoo's egg in the nest of a pair of icterine warblers. After the disturbance I had caused, one of the parents came back and hurriedly settled on the eggs, but on returning later I found that the European cuckoo's egg had disappeared while the birds were still incubating their own.

The resemblance of the European cuckoo's egg to those of the birds which hatch it may certainly be regarded as the result of natural selection. The eggs of each female European cuckoo seem to be always of one color type, and she presumably chooses to lay them in nests of the species by which she was herself reared. A hen European cuckoo reared by a white-throat is living proof that the egg from which she hatched is acceptable to white-throats. If we suppose that her own eggs resemble her mother's, she is assured of a home for her own offspring in the nests of the same species. Of course, we have to assume that the color of the eggs is inherited through the mother and not through the father, but this seems quite possible.

Some songbirds that have to put up with European cuckoos have gradually acquired the knack of distinguishing their own eggs—an ability that must be of considerable advantage to the species. Birds which do not discriminate at all, such as the reed warbler, are in certain areas threatened with extinction, for each year they raise a young European cuckoo instead of their own kind. Species which the European cuckoo does not bother obviously do not need to be able to recognize their own eggs. This may be why some birds, as we have already remarked, will sit on things like stones or bottles.

The European cuckoo is in some ways unusual. Many other kinds of parasitic cuckoos lay in the nests of only one or two host-species, and their eggs resemble these birds' eggs very closely both in color and in size. The southern great spotted cuckoo is somewhat larger than the common cuckoo and lays an egg that is excessively big in comparison. She lays in the nests of the hooded crow and of a kind of magpie, and her half-ounce egg is in between the weights of the eggs of these species. This cuckoo also often lays more than one egg in a nest, but the young do not throw out their nest-mates, and it does not seem to worry the foster parents that there are one or two extra children to rear.

In addition to parasitic cuckoos some other birds do not trouble to build their own nests and instead get strangers to hatch their eggs. Among these are the African honey-guides, the American cowbirds, at least some of the African whydahs (which are really weaver birds), and a South American duck. It seems that these young parasites generally hatch out before their foster companions; those which are reared with the host's own family are usually marked inside the gape and on the back so that they look like the host's young. The duck lays its eggs by preference in the nest of a raptor, but also at times in other ducks' nests; when the ducklings hatch, they leave the nest and join a duck family if they do not already belong to one. Since these strange young are readily accepted when they try to attach themselves to another family, they have no need for a special disguise like that of the other species.

Since the European cuckoo is raised by small birds which could hardly feed this gigantic youngster along with their own brood, the rightful nestlings have to be got rid of. This has led to a remarkable kind of behavior which may seem rather repulsive to us but is essential for the cuckoo's survival.

A few hours after it is hatched, the completely naked and blind young European cuckoo suddenly acquires the urge to throw out of the nest everything it can find, including, of course, eggs and other young. It pushes sideways and backwards under a nest-mate or under an egg, works the object onto its broad, slightly hollowed back, and supports it with its outstretched wings, which are far stronger and more dexterous than the wings of most small birds. The cuckoo then climbs backwards up the wall of the nest, using its head and neck as a prop—as can be seen in Figure 29, which was drawn from life. The little blind porter carries his burden to the rim of the nest and has to use all his skill not to fall out himself. When the job is done, he works his way back into the nest to tackle the next load.

If you want to see all this, just bring a nest with a young European cuckoo into the house and put a few small eggs or nestlings in with it. I have made movies of the whole process and find that people are always fascinated when they see it. But with their human ideas of right and wrong they always pity the rightful owners instead of admiring the cuckoo's intricate, and as yet unexplained, behavior.

The young cuckoo's urge to throw things out disappears after about four days. By this time it will have thrown out everything it does not approve of. It is not true, as has sometimes been said, that the other nestlings are squeezed out of the nest as the cuckoo grows older and larger—and yet one comes across such nonsense again and again.

People used to think that all an animal's actions are consciously performed. This led scientists to doubt the very

FIG. 29. A young European cuckoo throws its foster parents' egg out of the nest.

fact of the young European cuckoo's behavior; such a young creature, they said, could not in the first two or three days of its life have the premeditation and persistence to act in this way. We might just as well say that a nursing child cannot digest milk because it doesn't know that to do so it must secrete rennet, pepsin, and hydrochloric acid. Anyone who will take the trouble to watch a young European cuckoo can convince himself that it really does throw out eggs and nestlings as I have described.

I once found a garden warbler's nest with a European cuckoo's egg in it. When I visited the nest after the eggs had hatched, I found two 2-day-old warblers lying on the edge of the nest. They had been dead about twelve hours. Between them one of the parents was keeping the young cuckoo warm. The fact that the bird was quietly brooding its gawky stepchild beside the corpses of its own two children is a striking proof of how unconscious such birds are of the aims of reproduction. The warbler, we feel, would speedily bring its own young back into the nest and either throw out the intruder or peck it to death— which it certainly could do without difficulty. In reality, the parent is simply no longer aware of its dying children, for its urge to feed and warm little birds is completely satisfied by the stepchild.

During its stay of about three weeks in the nest the young European cuckoo is, unlike most other nestlings, remarkably inactive. It moves its head but does not thresh about with wings or feet; the warbler's flimsy nest would collapse if the cuckoo moved around very much.

Now, one more word about the "fraud" to which the foster parents, who have to feed the "insatiable" European cuckoo child, fall victim. First, the example of the warblers shows that the parents care very little about raising their own young, as long as they have young of some kind to raise. Second, the growing cuckoo does not require any more food than six young wagtails, who among them have a much larger area of body surface and therefore lose heat faster than a single cuckoo—and who presumably burn up food even more quickly because they are more active. Furthermore, after the young wagtails leave the nest they scatter so that the parents must search all over the place to find and feed them; it must be much easier to have only one fledgling to locate. One even gets the impression that the feeding behavior of the foster parents is more strongly aroused by the cuckoo than by their own young; at any rate, they seem quite engrossed in feeding it. One can be sure that if it were not a pleasure to bring up the young cuckoo they would not do so, for birds are not under the compulsion of a moral code.

When you bring a newly fledged European cuckoo into an aviary you can count on it that the other birds will soon start to feed the stranger—even though they may be hardly able to feed themselves. Some young Old World flycatchers proved this to me; in fact I had to move them out lest the hungry little chap attach itself to them instead of to me. Small birds that cannot reach up to the mouth of a young cuckoo often perch on its head or hover in front of it in order to put the food in properly (Fig. 30).

FIG. 30. A spotted flycatcher feeds a young European cuckoo without landing.

11. *Hybrids and Intersexes*

Many bird-fanciers cross canaries with other birds, usually with male European siskins or European goldfinches. If a siskin is the father, the offspring are usually a rather dull green. The goldfinch cross is more brightly colored, for the red of the goldfinch's face often shows up and the rest of his gay color pattern is at least sketched. (This only happens if the mother is as nearly as possible pure yellow, instead of the gray-green color of wild females.)

These crosses or hybrids—at least the females—are mostly sterile, but crossing with a serin, which is a much closer relative of the canary, results in young that can reproduce. We can say in general that crosses between closely related birds beget fertile offspring, while more distant relatives produce infertile young. Hybrids between any of the true pheasants, such as the Mongolian pheasant, the Chinese ring-necked pheasant, or any of the other forms of *Phasianus,* can reproduce perfectly well. The same is true of the offspring of the two species of *Chrysolophus,* the golden and Lady Amherst's pheasants, and for the various kaleege pheasants. On the other hand, although you can get a cross between a *Phasianus* and a *Chrysolophus* pheasant (if you give them no other choice) or even between a pheasant and a domestic hen, the hybrids are sterile.

Both peacocks and domestic cocks are known to mate successfully with guineafowl hens, but the offspring show no sexual behavior because their sex glands hardly develop at all. Such hybrids are sometimes mentally abnormal and are always undistinguished in color; instead of being the sum of their two parents, so to speak, they are an unseemly mosaic of both. The breeding dress of the peacock and the elegant spotting of the guineafowl are the result of inherited factors from two birds of the same species; since the hybrids get only one dose of inheritance for either species, the characteristics of each parental type tend to be diluted.

Pairing a strikingly colored mallard drake with a wood duck, or vice versa, does not produce the beautiful drakes one might hope for, with the markings and iridescent colors of both species. Instead, the sons are a uniform chocolate-brown with a slight gloss—and sterile as well, for mallards and wood ducks are only distant cousins. But if you interbreed various river and pond ducks (dabbling ducks) the progeny are fertile; this is true for example of the children of mallards and spot-billed ducks, or of mallards and pintails.

Remarkably enough, fertile hybrids have been produced from crossing the European spoonbill and sacred ibis, which belong to the same group but do not seem to be very closely related. There are even "three-quarter blooded" ibises or spoonbills which come from pairing these children with one of the parent species.

Strange love affairs sometimes result when birds are kept caged together for a long time. For instance a brightly colored rainbow lorikeet (a parrot) and a European purple gallinule or porphyrio (a rail) have been known to pair. The fact that both have blue feathers may have caused the mutual attraction. Even more bizarre was a white peacock at the Schönbrunn Zoo in Vienna, which was reared with giant Galapagos tortoises and thereafter refused to bestow his affections on anything else.

When very distantly related species are crossed, the hybrids are mainly male. We do not know however whether the eggs with the males in them are the only ones that develop to hatching, or whether only male eggs are laid.

These few examples show that birds, especially certain types, are more likely than mammals to form mixed pairs. Among birds, which often form a lasting pair bond, personal acquaintance between the mates is more important than among mammals, whose males do not help in tending the young.

One can say in general that birds which pair easily with one another and whose hybrid young are fertile are closely related, sometimes even geographical representatives of the same species. And vice versa: if two forms copulate only under special conditions—for instance in captivity when there is no mate of the right species—and any offspring which may result are infertile, then the forms are distantly related. There are, of course, exceptions such as the spoonbill-ibis cross already mentioned.

The cross between a capercaillie and a black grouse, which sometimes occurs in nature, was thought to be sterile. But a Swedish bird-fancier has crossed a one-year-old male hybrid (out of a capercaillie by a male black grouse) with a three-year-old capercaillie. She laid four eggs, all of which hatched, but two of the chicks died immediately and the others died fifty-five days later when they were given some worm medicine.

It is very surprising that, despite reports to the contrary, there are no known hybrids of mandarin ducks. The females of the East Asiatic mandarin duck and the North American wood duck are very like each other: both species nest in holes, their voices are somewhat alike, and the males of both species have an elaborate breeding plumage (Figs. 18 and 88). They are representatives of a group of ducks quite distant from the dabbling ducks mentioned above. If you keep them together, either in a big cage where they can fly or in the open, they almost always form mixed wood-mandarin duck pairs. The members of these pairs are extremely fond of each other: they go nest-hunting together and copulate, and the female lays her usual number of eggs in a hollow tree. It is clear that they consider each other of equal status and a suitable match, but unfortunately, the eggs are always infertile. If there are no others of their species around, you can mate wood ducks of either sex with widgeons, mallards, Bahama pintails, or pochards; the eggs hatch out, but the young are sterile. Mandarin ducks readily pair with small domestic ducks and others, but in this case the eggs never hatch. A female dwarf duck (a breed of mallard produced by man) always has infertile eggs when mated to a mandarin duck, although he may tread her many times; so does a female mandarin duck mated to another species. This inability of the mandarin duck to reproduce with other species is particularly puzzling, since ducks, like various gamebirds, produce hybrids fairly easily.

In birds and insects one sometimes finds individuals that have male sex organs on one side of the body and female on the other. If they are passerines or woodpeckers, in which the two sexes look different, the birds will be male-colored on one side and female on the other—a remarkable sight. I had a bullfinch of this sort with one side of the breast red and the other pale gray with a brownish sheen. People used to think it at one moment a male, at the next a female, as it hopped to and fro in its cage.

These harlequins, with their sharply divided right-and-left coloring, apparently do not occur in all birds; else they would have been noticed among the millions of wild ducks and pheasants, to say nothing of domestic chickens, that come to market.

We might suppose that since a bird's ovary is always on the left side this side would always be female-colored. But individuals have been seen with the ovary on the left and the testis on the right but with their feathering the other way round, male on the left and female on the right.

12. *Mating and Pairing*

In anything to do with love we are inclined to be anthropomorphic and form moral judgments. But we must avoid this and try for once to consider objectively everything to do with mating—and, if it occurs, with pairing —to see how it helps the species to survive. When I say that two birds are paired, I mean that they know one another and live together for weeks or months or years, and at some time indulge in sexual behavior together.

Birds' sex glands, or gonads, are located in the body cavity just above the kidneys. After the breeding season, when they are extremely swollen, they shrink until hardly visible. This waxing and waning of the gonads fundamentally alters the bird's state of mind so that in winter many species are effectively sexless. One cannot therefore talk about the faithfulness or unfaithfulness in winter of two birds which formed a pair the previous spring. This is particularly true of most migratory birds. The mates often set off separately to winter in the tropics, and the following spring they return separately to their former breeding place, the males a week or two before the females. Such birds are paired for only about three months of the year, and it is quite unimportant to them whether or not they get the same mate the next year; they only care that they have some kind of a mate to help them raise a couple of broods before the autumn. Such birds are faithful to a nesting place, returning there year after year, rather than to another individual.

Birds like barn swallows, which often nest in colonies and rear two or three broods between May and August, sometimes change mates between broods. The important thing for the species is that eight to ten young are raised every year, for the birds must suffer considerable losses each season from enemies and the weather. The individual barn swallow does not care with whom it mates and rears young, but only that it does it as quickly as possible; the summer is short, and the winter quarters are for molting, not breeding. One reason why the pairs sometimes break up between broods may be that the new breeding cycle of each partner is not quite synchronized with its mate's; it is better that each should choose a new partner in the right stage. At any rate we know for certain from studies of thousands of banded barn swallows that there is frequently a change of mates.

A study of storks has shown the same thing. The farmer swears that every year the same pair of storks nests on his farmhouse; but scientists, who have marked many storks with numbered bands that can be read at a distance with a telescope, must contradict this legend.

What usually happens is this. At the end of March or early in April a male stork, who is three or fours years old and ready to breed, appears alone on the nest. He leaves it only briefly to feed, lest someone else occupy it. A week or two later a female appears and is received with excited bill-clattering (Fig. 69), in which she joins the male. They soon copulate, and when the eggs have been laid both parents take turns incubating. The male seems to sit on the eggs more often during the day and the female at night. The sexes are difficult to distinguish, and when one reads in the newspaper about the "hen brooding on the nest" this is because the reporter's wife takes care of his children.

It may happen that an unmated male stork, recognizable from his band number as having bred there before, is joined by a female who is not his previous mate; he will accept her just as happily as his former wife. And it is just the same for the female: she returns to the nesting place slightly later than the male and will go to any suitable male of her species without regard to who he is. Should it happen that a male's wife of the previous year returns after he has been joined by another female, there is a tremendous fight between the two females. The male merely watches without joining in—it's all the same to him so long as there is one female to help him produce more storks. Of course, the male does not take into consideration the survival of the species, but the species does in fact survive because he takes the very first mate that will breed with him.

Birds that do not migrate may behave differently. A pair of ravens, for instance, remain together all winter, living in a large area centered on the nest.

Most of the birds whose pairing habits have been mentioned so far in this chapter are monogamous—that is to say, for each brood they stick to one mate whom they know personally, and they do not tolerate any third bird near the nest. Instead of asking if a bird is monogamous or polygamous, it is more to the point to ask if one or both parents are necessary for rearing the young. Birds like the passerines and storks, whose young have to be fed for a time in the nest, nearly always have some kind of marriage because one parent cannot manage alone. On the other hand, birds whose young are to some extent independent from the start may or may not have a lasting bond between the sexes.

Sometimes male and female only meet for the act of copulation and remain separate for the rest of the year. This is typical of those birds which have very elaborate displays and in which the sexes often differ very strikingly in color, shape, and weight. For most of the year both the black grouse and capercaillie live celibately in loose flocks. At the beginning of the breeding season each male searches out a display place where he per-

FIG. 31. Male black grouse displaying.

forms very peculiar movements and calls (Fig. 31).
Females that are ready to mate come to the males, which
court and mount as many hens as they can. The females
then retire to lay their eggs, hatch them out, and lead
the young about, while the males, which know nothing
of such cares, again form into flocks. The following
spring there is the same performance, and it is pure
chance whether the same hen goes to the same cock. Who
knows if they can even recognize each other again? In
species like these one cannot really talk about a lasting
bond, let alone monogamy or polygamy, for the male
and female never develop any relationship except the act
of copulation.

With geese it is just the opposite. A graylag gander, a
year and a half old, pays his court by posturing in a
special way to a particular goose; since she belongs to a
different family, which would drive him away if he went
to her, he must from a distance induce her to leave her
family and join him. During the winter he wins her over
and they form a pair without any sexual behavior. Their
engagement is finally clinched when they perform together their characteristic triumph ceremony after driving away an opponent—they are then united against the
world. So long as the gander defends the goose, first as
his betrothed and later as his wife, and so long as he is
a loving father to their children, the pair stay together—
without separating in winter as most songbirds do. The

reason for this is mainly that the young have much to learn and are looked after by their parents for almost a year, until the breeding season comes round again (Fig. 32). This kind of pairing depends on more than sexual activity, and the personality of the mate plays a great part. Sometimes after the death of one mate the widowed survivor does not pair again. We tend to think of such behavior as beautifully moral—in fact, it is an evolutionary dead end which might lead the species to extinction.

When birds do not pair at all and only one parent hatches the eggs, this may be either the father or the mother. The job falls to the male in the South American tinamous, the emus (Fig. 25), the cassowaries, the rheas (the South American ostrich-like birds), the button quail, and various waders; the males of these species are often smaller and less conspicuous than the females. In gamebirds and waterfowl, in which the sexes are differently colored, it is the female, again the parent with the more somber plumage, who takes care of the brood.

A number of dabbling ducks and diving ducks pair in

FIG. 32. A pair of graylag geese defend their family together.

the autumn but separate as soon as the eggs are laid in the spring, the drake taking no part in the incubating. Many drakes have an orgy from March on, trying to rape every female they meet with no intention of forming any lasting ties. They even go so far as to reject the invitations of their wives. Female ducks are uncommonly faithful; in their determination to avoid the strange Don Juans they will die rather than be ravished.

Mallards which have settled in large city parks are fairly easy to observe, since they are not afraid of us the way most wild animals are. Anyone who has visited these parks during the spring, from about the middle of March to the end of May, will have seen three mallards overhead, flying one behind the other. The foremost, a female, utters her long drawn-out alarm call, and there are two drakes behind her. You may think it is two males chasing an unmated female. The truth is that a faithful female is being hounded by a strange male, and her husband has to follow along in order to locate his wife when the wild pursuit is over. The fourth duck involved, the wife of the importunate pursuer, stays behind where the affair began, ignoring the whole disorderly scene. She spends her time looking for the large amount of food she will need to produce her thirteen eggs in as many days.

Meanwhile, another drake or two may have joined in the chase with the same lecherous intent. The incident ends when the strange drakes, without ever getting what they want, have had enough and fly back to their lawful wives. These females recognize their husbands from afar —one wonders how—and join them, whereas on the approach of a strange drake they remain silent on the water or hide in the reeds. It may be added that these birds, which all look alike to us, can tell one another apart by their faces.

As early as September many dabbling ducks start to copulate with their legitimate mates. Earlier, when the drake sometimes has not yet completed his display plumage, the female takes the part of the wooer, for such a male is not yet in the mood for love and avoids bodily contact, making up, one might say, all sorts of excuses to repulse the advances of his wife: he has to drive away an enemy (who does not exist), has to take a bath, or has something else that he simply must do. Such copulations, of course, have nothing to do with reproduction, for the birds' sex glands are very small and undeveloped until spring.

In autumn and winter there is none of the chasing of strange females by drakes. Instead, the birds gather into small courtship parties which result in the males getting themselves wives. Those females which are still unmated try to call down other mallards with a loud, ringing crescendo "Quack quaak quak quak-quak." This cry is, of course, heard no more after the beginning of spring, when it might attract an unwanted lover.

Since these pairs form in the autumn and winter, often far from the breeding grounds in regions as remote as the Nile, it may happen that a female from England follows her new husband to Siberia, or vice versa. A constant mingling of North European ducks takes place so that no geographical races develop. This is not true of the many other birds that migrate to Africa independently of their mates and pair only when they return again to the breeding place—for instance the shrikes, which winter in East Africa, and the European swifts.

The number of times a pair of birds copulate has no bearing on the number of eggs they produce. A pair of griffon vultures will perform for months at very short intervals and finally lay only one egg, while a single mating suffices for a turkey hen to lay twelve to fifteen eggs.

The turkey, German grouse, peacock, and Argus pheasant do not pair. The cocks set aside special mating hours and do not pursue hens out of hours. The hens approach the cocks only when ready to be mounted, expressing their willingness to oblige by making special movements.

We can say on the whole that a lasting pairing takes place in birds which share the responsibilities of brooding or which stay around the nesting place outside the breeding season. We have seen this in geese and ravens. Domestic pigeons are the same way. The well-known sociability of these birds and of their wild ancestors, the rock doves, is not a case of mutual friendliness; it is just that they feel safer in a flock, and by watching their companions they can take advantage of any food or water the others find. Single individuals cannot stand each other, but married couples proverbially get on very well together (for pigeons and doves are the same thing): neither tries to snatch the other's food, and they like to sit together side by side, caressing each other's neck feathers. You never see this in strange pigeons, which always keep out of reach of each other's beak. After raising one brood successfully the pigeon starts again with the same mate, and this goes on year after year.

The average pigeon pairing is something like this. A male, just become adult, finds a nesting place in some dark corner of a dovecote and sits there calling monotonously hour after hour, "Roo, roo, roo." At intervals he blows up his neck, spreads his tail, and turns round and round calling "Wung wung ruckoo" to the females. When a female finally sidles up to him, he promptly throws her out of the nest. The female, undeterred, keeps coming back until at last he lets her stay. She celebrates her success by hopping around in a peculiar way with her tail spread out on the ground. This is the sign that the pair are united, and from this time on they sit in the nest caressing one another for half an hour at a time. No other pigeon is allowed near the nest, and this often leads to fierce battles. Even when they leave the nest, the pair stays together, continually following each other with their eyes.

After a while the cock begins "driving" the hen. He follows at her heels wherever she goes, pecks at her if she stands still, and will hardly let her eat and drink. To us humans this seems anything but affectionate, for the female simply cannot get away from her husband. But if his interest is diverted from her for a moment and he does not follow, instead of flying away she looks round until he catches up and starts hounding her again. The female gets no peace until she is back in the nest; then he starts to caress her. In human language this means, "Be good and stay at home and no more gadding about!" As they sit on the edge of the nest the male will suddenly fly down with a great fuss and commotion; if all is well, she follows him, but with less excitement.

Some days previously, perhaps during the driving, the mating preliminaries will have begun. The female suddenly stops still, the pair stare at each other, and then one or other, usually the male, looks over its shoulder and passes its beak under one wing. Then the hen goes to the cock and they bill, which is the same action you see when an adult pigeon feeds its young: the female pushes her beak inside the male's, making him regurgitate. For several minutes this feeding goes on, alternating with the twitch at the wing. Finally the female crouches and the male mounts her. This whole show is sometimes repeated briefly with roles reversed, the male crouching and the female mounting him in the normal way. In certain wild Australian pigeons this reversal regularly follows the normal mounting and is often repeated. After a successful copulation the female runs a few steps with her tail fanned out and pressed on the ground; then the male flies off and she follows him.

After about a week of this business the male suddenly starts bringing material for the nest while the female sits in the nestcup and pushes the twigs under herself. Within a few days she lays her first egg late one afternoon. Both parents guard it in turn, until two days later, shortly after midday, the second egg appears and the seventeen-day period of real incubation begins.

The cock pigeon incubates from morning to afternoon, the hen the rest of the time. In the wild the birds spend their time off looking for food, for one mate does not feed the other on the nest as do so many birds of prey, parrots, and certain songbirds. In some pigeons the change-over at the nest is organized on a very rigid schedule; others seem to realize that something is wrong if, during their time off, they meet their mate away from the nest, and they fly back to cover the eggs even though it is not their turn. Black-crowned night-herons have been seen to do the same thing.

If one mate dies or is hurt and does not return to the nest, the other usually incubates two days and then deserts the nest. This seems purely automatic, for I have seen a male brood his allotted two days although his wife lay dead in front of the nest. Pigeons obviously do not know what death means. After such a misfortune the survivor quickly pairs again—if it is still the breeding season and if he or she can find a suitable mate—and starts off a new brood.

If at any time during the ten-day copulation period the male is not quite up to the mark, the female lets another male—often a particular favorite—mount her. Every off-duty female is mildly accosted by almost every off-duty male, but this does not mean much more than "Good-day to you, madam." At any rate, if she goes on her way, he does not pester her any more. But if this is just what she wants and she obligingly crouches, the male's politeness turns to embarrassment, for he needs a little time until he comes into the right mood to oblige her. Even then, the mating is without the tenderness usual between married pigeons. The female then goes back contentedly to the nest and is otherwise faithful to her husband, who for his part goes on to raise the family with her as if nothing had happened. If differently colored birds are kept together, we can sometimes tell from the color of her children whether a female has strayed from virtue.

All the doves and pigeons of the world, including the domestic pigeon, manufacture a kind of food in their crops which is fed by both parents to the young when they are small. Shortly before the young hatch, there appears in the crops of the parents a whitish porridge, which consists of cells released from the lining of the crop. The little squab in its yellowish down, helpless and blind (Fig. 33), sticks its bill into the throat of its mother or father and they pump this crop-milk into it by making retching movements. When the chick is five days old, it gets its first grain to eat, at first softened and mixed with the milk, but the parents go on producing the crop-milk and mixing it with the other food for about eighteen days. These figures apply only to domestic pigeons; in many wild species the young are kept on pure crop-milk for a much longer time. We can let domestic pigeons hatch these wild species, but if they are allowed to feed them for long, the young die of severe inflammations of the crop; they cannot live on a diet of grain as early as can the domestic pigeon and possibly its ancestor, the rock dove.

Even when the young pigeons have left the nest and are able to peck for themselves, they still for a few days get part of their food from their parents' throats. For this reason the feathers between their eyes and beak grow very late; otherwise they would get all stuck together. The same is true of European cormorants, which feed from their parents in the same way.

FIG. 33. Rock dove egg and newly hatched squab. About one half natural size.

From spring to midsummer both wild and domestic pigeons dovetail successive broods; if all goes well a wood pigeon or stock dove can raise as many as four broods in a season. The young are warmed by their parents for about a week; then the adults begin to look around for a new nesting place, and drive and caress again; and this all leads up to the building of a new nest. In fact, a pair of pigeons with young not quite ready to fly in one nest often have eggs in another. The young of the first brood are only just independent when the second lot hatches.

Domestic pigeons that are well fed and kept warm and protected from the vagaries of the climate multiply more quickly than the wild birds, many of which migrate in autumn to warmer regions.

Obviously there are many other patterns of reproduction than those sketched here; one must always be cautious of generalizations from these few examples.

13. *Eggs, Young, and Growth*

A bird's egg consists of a shell of chalky material with a thin skin under it, and inside that the transparent white in which the yolk floats. Tortoises and crocodiles have the same sort of egg; those of other reptiles consist of a flexible parchment-like envelope filled with a uniform mixture of yolk and white.

The shell of a bird's egg may be uniformly colored or heavily spotted, rough or smooth, thick or thin. These qualities vary with the group and usually have some value. The color often depends on whether the bird needs camouflage, and the thickness of the shell on how roughly the bird treats its eggs. The spurred, strong-footed African francolin has eggs you can practically bounce off a wall, while the careful ducks and waders, with their delicate legs and beaks, have eggs with very thin shells.

Just one example: The European curlew weighs about 2¼ pounds; and its egg, which takes 29½ days to hatch, weighs 2½ ounces when fresh, as much as a very large hen's egg. But never give one to a hen to hatch. Everything goes well as long as the air pocket at the blunt end is small. Later, towards the end of incubation, it is nearly inevitable that even the most careful little hen will stave in the blunt end; the air space has grown bigger, and there is no longer a cushion of egg-white to support the shell, which itself is not thick enough to withstand the pressure of the foster mother's bony legs. For this reason I do not generally leave a curlew's egg to be hatched by a hen but remove it after a time to the incubator.

The shape of the egg usually has a purpose. The murre's egg (Fig. 34) is conical to prevent it from rolling off the rock ledges where the bird breeds. The four eggs of a lapwing or plover are so big that in order to fit under the bird they have to be arranged with their pointed ends together (Fig. 35). If you change their position the bird will come back and rearrange them as before. When the clutch consists of many eggs, it does not help much for them to be pointed; they are usually rounder (Fig. 14*a*). In this way the dozen or so eggs of a pheasant, a partridge, or a duck are packed into the nest.

The egg-white varies in quantity and consistency in different groups of birds. The embryo uses it to grow on and as a water store, so that unlike the yolk it is completely used up before the bird hatches.

The amount of yolk in proportion to the whole egg varies greatly. In eggs that I have weighed, the proportion varies from 15 per cent for the wryneck and European cormorant to about 50 per cent in some ducks. In general, the eggs of birds like passerines and pigeons, from which the young hatch in a relatively undeveloped

FIG. 34. Egg of a murre. Two-fifths natural size.

FIG. 35. The clutch of a little ringed plover.

stage, have about 20 per cent yolk, while those whose young are active soon after hatching—such as gamebirds and ducks—have something like 35 per cent (Fig. 36).

Nestlings such as cormorants and woodpeckers, which are helpless at first and are fed by their parents, come from eggs with a minute amount of yolk which is almost all used up before they hatch. But a third of the huge yolk in a swan's or diving duck's egg remains at hatching inside the chick's body as a provision for the first days of its life, for the tiny creature is not fed by its parents and is often unable to look for food because of the cold or rain. Indeed some species have to make a long journey to find a lake with a suitable food supply. If you take one of these active, independent little fellows into the house, you soon find that it uses the first days to look for food and examine it, without really eating anything. During this time when it is feeding on the remains of the yolk, it develops in body and mind but does not get much heavier.

Compared with mammals, reptiles, and most amphibians and fishes, a bird grows up very quickly, attaining adult weight much earlier than these other animals. This is certainly an adaptation to flying, for the great majority of birds do not molt their wing-feathers during their first

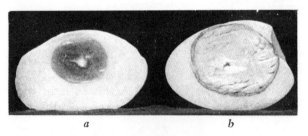

FIG. 36. Hard-boiled eggs cut in half. *a* Egg of the crowned eagle hawk (young helpless at hatching). *b* Egg of the snow goose (active soon after hatching). About one-half natural size.

FIG. 37. A juvenile European black-bird, 31 days old, sunning itself. One-fourth natural size.

year and therefore cannot adjust the lifting surface of their wings to changes in their body weight. This explanation of the rule is proved by the exceptions: the birds that never fly, like the ostriches and cassowaries; and birds like the gamebirds, which instead of getting one set of wing-feathers to last them for their first year have a juvenal molt of these flight-feathers and so can adjust their wing-area to a slower increase in weight. This special molt of young gamebirds will be considered in the next chapter.

Feathers stop growing when the shafts have become quite horny and lost their supply of blood vessels. Birds the size of a thrush or smaller take about a month for the full complement of wing-feathers to grow to full size (Fig. 37). By this time the bird has reached approximately its adult body weight. There are even birds, like the barn swallow, that weigh slightly more just before they leave the nest at three weeks old than they do later. A newly hatched barn swallow weighs about a twentieth of an ounce. At 5 days it weighs 6 times as much, at 10 days, 14 times, and at 15 days, 14½ times. But its parents weigh about two-thirds of an ounce, only 11 to 12 times as much as the newly hatched nestling.

In ten days the longest wing-feathers of the barn swallow sprout from less than an inch to over two inches long, growing at more than one-tenth of an inch a day. Compare this with your finger nails, which grow one twenty-fifth as fast. The flight-feathers of large birds like cranes and some geese and swans grow more than a third of an inch a day.

The rate at which the body and feathers grow depends on how the bird lives and its evolutionary history. Young barn swallows and European swifts, which nest high up, must go a good distance on their very first flight. But birds nesting on the ground or in reeds or bushes can afford to leave the nest without being able to fly properly so long as they can scramble about and find cover and protection close around the nest. The same is true of some water birds, particularly swans and grebes.

It makes a big difference whether or not a bird is able to run about as soon as it is hatched. Those that have to

a

FIG. 38*a*. A helpless nestling stork 1½ days old. One half natural size.
FIG. 38*b*. A stork at 29 days with its wing-feathers sprouting. About one-tenth natural size.

b

leave the nest right away and run after their parents through thick and thin have well developed legs, but their wings grow slowly. On the other hand, birds that are fed by their parents in the nest develop their legs late—to keep the helpless little nestlings from climbing out—but their wing-feathers develop very early.

This difference can be seen at once if you compare the growth of storks and cranes, which are as adults rather similar in shape (Figs. 38a and b, 39a and b, 43a, 68–69). Young cranes leave the nest early; their leg-bones, the so-called tarsi (singular: tarsus), grow fastest between the eighth and sixteenth days, at slightly more than a quarter of an inch a day. The young stork stays some time in the nest; the main growth of its tarsus comes later, between the twentieth and thirty-eighth days, with an increase of a little less than one-fifth of an inch a day. This is about the same relative increase, for the tarsus of an adult stork is about 7½ inches long, the adult crane's about 10 inches. Both birds, however, are pretty well grown at ten weeks and are able to fly.

FIG. 39a. A two-day-old crane, its legs already well developed. One-eighth natural size.
FIG. 39b. A crane at 32 days. Its legs have almost finished growing, but it has almost no wing-feathers. One-tenth natural size.

a   b

These are long-legged birds, but for the most long-legged of all we turn to the South Asiatic sarus crane, whose tarsus is 12½ inches, and the flamingos, of which I myself have measured leg-bones almost 14 inches long. There are, unfortunately, no records of the growth-rate of the leg-bones of these birds, but I would guess it must reach more than a third of an inch a day.

As usual, there is no hard and fast rule for the way a bird responds to the demands of its environment. There are birds that can run about soon after hatching and can fly very shortly afterwards, and there are birds that stay in the nest for some time but cannot fly when they leave it. Rails leave the nest early; and since they live in good cover, their wing-feathers grow very late, for they do not really need to fly until they migrate in the autumn. At five weeks the wing-feathers of the moorhen, which is

FIG. 40*a*. A moorhen at 31 days; its wing-feathers still tiny.

FIG. 40*b*. A lapwing at 28 days, almost ready to fly.

a kind of rail, are growing and still short in their sheaths (Fig. 40*a*), while at the same age the considerably larger lapwing, which lives more in the open and has to be able to get away from enemies, has been able to fly for a long time (Fig. 40*b*).

Birds that eat only meat or fish are little troubled with indigestible matter, so that most of their food goes for growth. A female goshawk which ate about five and a half ounces of pure meat a day, and a three-week-old stork which ate 17½ ounces of meat and fish a day, both used a third of this food to increase their weight. The same proportion applies to other young birds of fairly large size which are kept on such a diet.

The young bird that has been fed in the nest by its parents for days or weeks loses its appetite shortly before leaving the nest. In some species it takes no food at all at this time and becomes restless until it has flown, whereupon its appetite returns again. Some people think the parents try to tempt the young out of the nest with food; from my own experience in raising birds I have come to think that even though the young at this time make begging movements, you cannot get them to take any food. This is true not only for songbirds but for eagles, owls, and many others.

14. Molting

The outside covering of mammals and birds is exposed to so much wear and tear that it has to be renewed. This can either go on continuously, a little at a time —as happens with our skin and nails, with hooves, and with the beak and claws of birds—or it can happen abruptly, every now and then, as with hair and feathers. A roe-deer changes its short, red summer hair in autumn for a long, thick, gray winter coat. Feathers are molted in exactly the same way.

Most birds keep the whole plumage for a year, but some renew it twice yearly. Many others molt the small body-feathers twice a year but the large wing- and tail-feathers only once. The cranes and the eagle owl seem to be the only birds that keep their wing-feathers for two years at a time.

During the process of changing feathers which we call molting, a new feather grows deep in the skin under the old dead one. As it grows the new feather pushes out its predecessor and finally takes its place. A single papilla or feather germ can produce different sorts of feather, depending on the age of the bird and the time of year. This explains how the inconspicuous plumage, sometimes called the winter plumage, can change into the display or summer dress of the breeding season. Many birds lose their display feathers before incubation begins; others, including many brightly colored male ducks, lose them only for a short time at the end of the breeding season.

As a rule, the molt takes place gradually, following a set pattern, so that the bird is never naked or unable to fly. This is what happens in raptors, pigeons, parrots, gulls, gamebirds, and the familiar passerines. When they are molting, most birds lead a quiet, rather withdrawn life, since all their energy must go into renewing their feathers and they do not feel quite up to par. Molting is, of course, not a disease but a regular physiological process which has a great effect on the bird's metabolism, especially if the molt is rapid.

Since feathers not only keep out the cold, like the hair of mammals, but also help birds to fly or swim, the way the different feathers succeed each other differs greatly from species to species. We can only give a hint of this variety.

The simplest molt is the penguin's (Fig. 41): it loses its feathers almost all at once, and you see it standing quietly in the middle of a heap of them. Fourteen days

FIG. 41. Molting king penguins with their young. These birds lose all their feathers at the same time, the new feathers appearing beneath the old ones. (Courtesy of the American Museum of Natural History.)

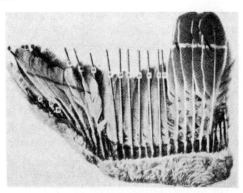

FIG. 42. A molting goose's wing. Sticks show the places where the wing-feathers have fallen out.

or so later the new plumage has grown, and it is able to enter the water once more. During this time it cannot catch food, but it has a good layer of fat to tide it over until it can feed again. This simple form of molting is possible for the penguin because it has no long flight-feathers to grow, and the small body-feathers need only a little time to mature.

Some birds lose all their flight-feathers at the same time and are unable to fly for some weeks. These are always birds that can retire to inaccessible places like reed-beds and marshes or open water. They include all geese (Fig. 42), ducks, and swans, as well as grebes, loons, rails, most auks, almost all cranes (Figs. 43*a* and *b*), flamingos, and anhingas. It is significant that the demoiselle crane, the only crane that lives in steppe country without any cover, and the magpie goose, which practically never goes near the water, are exceptions in their groups and never become flightless.

It is hard to tell whether the first birds molted their wing-feathers gradually or simultaneously. But we do know that one of them, the fossil, reptile-like *Archaeopteryx* (Fig. 1), molted them gradually and was therefore never flightless. This can be clearly seen by studying the slab of slate in which this creature left its impression.

If the wing-feathers are all molted at once, the time this happens must be fitted in with the breeding cycle. In ducks, since the female alone takes care of the brood, the male molts before her, and she waits until the young birds have grown up a little. With swans it is the other way round. The female becomes flightless shortly after the eggs hatch, the male only later when his wife can again use her wings a little. Since the development of the young is so slow, the parents can take turns molting, so that one is always ready to herd and defend the cygnets. By late summer the whole family is able to fly and ready for the autumn migration.

It has been found that the female hornbill loses almost all her feathers during the weeks she is tending the young in the nest. But a male, or a female that is not breeding, molts without losing the power of flight. Almost all hornbills wall up the entrance to the nest-hole, which is in a tree or cliff, leaving only a small slit through which the male can feed his wife and children. During the time

FIG. 43*a*. A crane able to fly.

FIG. 43*b*. The same bird during the molt, when it cannot fly. The new flight-feathers can be seen, short and still growing.

there are eggs or young, the mother never leaves her voluntary prison and gets through her molt there—a most remarkable adaptation.

The great majority of birds lose their feathers gradually. Usually, the innermost primaries fall out first, and the other primaries follow in order toward the wing-tip (Fig. 44). The secondary feathers molt from both ends toward the middle. The molting of tail-feathers starts in some birds with the middle pair and moves outward, so that the outermost feathers are not shed until the new middle ones have finished growing. Other birds molt in exactly the reverse order, while in yet others the feathers fall out in succession but each only when its neighbor is almcst completely grown.

Woodpeckers and tree creepers, which use their tails to prop themselves up when they are climbing a tree, have a remarkable adaptation to keep this prop in use at all times. The tail-feathers completely overlap each other on each side, the central pair, which provide the main support, being on top (Fig. 45). The molt begins with the second pair from the inside and moves gradually

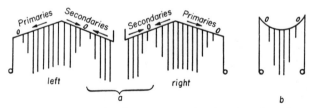

FIG. 44. Diagram of molting wings and tail to show how the gradual molt of these feathers takes place in most passerines and many other birds. Lines that have circles at the end show old feathers; lines without circles represent new feathers, the length of the line indicating how far the new feather has grown. *O* shows where an old feather has fallen out and the new one has not yet appeared. The arrows show the order in which the feathers molt.

(*a*) The molt of the wings. The molt is almost over. The last-but-one primary and the last secondary have fallen out but are not yet replaced.

(*b*) The molt of the tail. The next-to-outside tail-feathers have not yet been replaced.

FIG. 45. Middle spotted woodpecker. Note the tail-prop. About one-third natural size.

outward. Only after the outer pair has been replaced do the middle two feathers fall out. Since the other feathers now bear the weight of the bird, the middle pair can grow without being strained.

The fact that tree creepers go through exactly the same sort of molt as woodpeckers cannot be explained by relationship, for the tree creeper is a member of the passerines and shows few other resemblances to the woodpeckers, which belong to quite a different worldwide group. The similar molt is easily explained as a parallel adaptation, because both birds sit on their tails.

In raptors such as European sparrowhawks and ospreys the female, who does almost all the incubation and takes care of the small young, takes advantage of this inactive time to molt. The male must maintain his powers of flight fully intact so that he can bring in food during this period, and he waits to molt until the young have left the nest.

As has been mentioned, most gallinaceous birds can use their wings comparatively soon after they creep out of the egg; their special way of molting their wing-feathers keeps their wing-area in the right proportion to their weight as they grow up. At first, in addition to the secondaries, the chick has only seven or eight inner primaries (Figs. 46 and 13*b*), which soon reach their full size and form the first functional wings. As the outer primaries gradually grow, the inner ones are replaced, working outwards, by new feathers which last a year. Only the two wing-tip feathers, which are narrow and pointed in keeping with the small size of their owner, are not renewed. Their presence distinguishes a young bird up to a year old from its elders, which have broader, rounded wing-tip feathers, like those in the rest of the wing. Gallinaceous birds thus have one complete juvenal molt in their first year, except for these two outermost primaries.

The young bird's first feathers do not sprout at the same time all over its body; we can often make out separate outbursts of growth, although they are not always sharply distinct from one another. Obviously, there is not room on a young bird for as many feathers as its parents have. After a few weeks some birds lose these first scanty feathers of the juvenal plumage; they are replaced by feathers that are frequently like the adult's. In this molt the wing- and tail-feathers are often not involved; some finches and thrushes, for instance, keep the same wings and tail till they are one year old, while cranes keep their wing-feathers for two years.

FIG. 46. A three-day-old green peacock with wings already well developed. One-third natural size.

Other birds get a whole new plumage, including wing- and tail-feathers, in the first few months. The new feathers are sometimes a different color, longer, and more developed than the first ones. Some passerines go through this post-juvenal molt—European tree or house sparrows, larks, corn buntings, long-tailed tits, starlings, bearded tits, and snow-finches; so do pigeons and woodpeckers.

Most birds molt once a year, changing all their feathers. This is called the annual molt. Some birds have a partial molt as well. When a bird renews its wing- and tail-feathers, it always changes the rest of the plumage too, but the converse is not true.

When a feather is pulled out, the feather papilla starts to manufacture a new one at once. Of course, it takes a few days for the feather germ to develop enough to break through the skin; the time it takes for the feather to finish growing depends on its length. In Chapter 13 I have already mentioned how fast certain feathers grow.

The time a bird molts is often connected with the time it migrates. Three species of shrike that fly to Africa have an annual molt there at the turn of the year. But the northern shrike, which scarcely leaves its breeding area, has an annual molt at the end of the breeding season—in Germany some time in August.

Everything about the molt cannot be explained away in terms of its purpose; much is certainly the result of the ancestry of the species. Otherwise, it would be strange that the swift garganey drake should be tied to one place for four weeks while its wings molt, whereas its neighbor, the clumsy and melancholy bittern, never loses its power of flight though it can hardly be driven out of the thick reed-beds where it lives. And it must be a common heritage which makes almost all the birds that have a gradual wing-molt replace their primaries in much the same way—both the winter wren scuttling about our thickets and the albatross soaring for weeks on end over the southern oceans.

15. *Color and Pigment*

When a feather or a hair has no pigment in it, it looks white. This effect is produced by many tiny air-filled spaces that lie inside the horny material of which the feathers are made; it looks white for the same reason that foaming water looks white.

Most feathers contain some pigment. Usually, only what is visible is colored; the down and the lower part of the feather which is covered by its neighbors are whitish or a uniform dull gray. This proves that a bird's color and marking must be there to be seen, in other words, for some purpose.

A bird's color, whether it is the camouflage of a lark or the display plumage of a pheasant, can be produced in different ways. Dark shades are the result of granules of substances called eumelanin, reddish or yellowish tones by phaeomelanin. Bright yellow, red, and yellowish-red colors are produced by lipochromes, pigments soluble in fat.

Blue is usually what is called a structural color—the result of the structure of the feather backed up by a pigment. Inside a blue feather (Fig. 47) are many tiny, colorless, air-filled boxes whose walls (c) are pierced and made opaque by little air-canals; these cells, lying against a dark pigment (a), give the effect of blue. If the surrounding horny layer (b) is yellow, the feather looks green, for one is seeing the blue through a yellow filter. This is what makes the ordinary budgerigar seem green. Man has managed to breed blue budgerigars—these birds lack the yellow layer. If the dark brown background is missing, the feather looks yellow, while white budgerigars lack both pigments.

If you soak a blue feather in water until you get all the air out of the boxes, the feather looks blackish, just as it does when you hold it up and look at it against light. If a green parrot gets wet through, it looks gray-brown. A blue feather also loses its colors if you crush the air-filled boxes with a hammer.

In certain cases green is produced by a special lipochrome—one example is the remarkable apple-green on the back of the head of an eider drake.

The wings of many kinds of ducks have a patch of iridescent feathers called the speculum; the plumage of many other birds, including the peacock, is more or less iridescent. This effect is due to what are called interference colors, which are also responsible for the turquoise blue of the European kingfisher. These colors are produced by minute colorless plates, one ten-thousandth of an inch thick, which are set so as to reflect the light just as it is reflected in a soap-bubble, and give a delicate iridescence. In feathers a dark pigment lying beneath the little plates makes the effect possible.

Dark pigment also helps feathers to last better. This is why the large wing- and tail-feathers of almost all

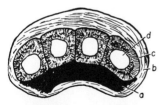

FIG. 47. A diagrammatic cross-section through one of the little branching elements in the web of a blue feather (greatly enlarged). Dark pigment (*a*) underlies the little boxes which consist of a central air-space (*d*), enclosed by thick horny walls (*c*), which are pierced by tiny air-passages. The whole thing is surrounded by a horny layer (*b*).

birds are black or grayish-brown. The stork, for instance, is pure white except for its black wings; so is the snow goose. There are also remarkable exceptions, in which the colors are exactly the other way around: the black swan, the saddle-billed and black-necked storks and the ground hornbills.

If a feather which is partly light and partly dark is exposed to a lot of wear, the yellowish or whitish parts will disintegrate in time. You see this in European curlews, bustards, many gulls, and raptors (Fig. 48), and in the feathers of the peacock's back. Some birds make use of this fact: the feathers newly acquired at the molt have white tips or fringes which gradually become rubbed off so that by spring the birds seem to have a completely new breeding plumage. By becoming shabbier, they become more handsome. The throat of the house sparrow (Fig. 49), the linnet's red color on its

FIG. 48. The pale spots on a falcon's tail-feathers have been worn away more than the darker parts. (Enlarged.)

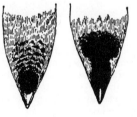

FIG. 49. On the left, the new throat-feathers of a male house sparrow. On the right, the same feathers after they have been worn.

FIG. 50. Fault-bars in the tail-feathers of a European blackbird. The blackbird was captured as it left the nest, when the feathers had reached about one-fourth their final length. For a few days the bird was poorly cared for, and the fault-bars appeared during this time. Later, the feathers resumed their normal growth.

head and breast, and the spring dress of the starling are good examples. When an adult male linnet gets his new plumage in the late summer, the beautiful red is already there, but it is hidden by a fine, grayish-yellow "fur" which is gradually worn off during the winter so that the red comes into view.

Weak spots on feathers can also be produced by illness. If a bird gets sick when it is molting or when its first plumage is growing, the sprouting feathers can be easily damaged. The tiny hooks which hold together the vane of the feather do not grow properly and so-called "fault-bars" appear in the feathers (Fig. 50). People who raise ostriches have a lot of trouble with this.

Feather pigments frequently become bleached during the course of the year. Black feathers may turn brown, and brown feathers cream-colored. In the green feathers of the bee-eater the superficial yellow pigment (in *b* in Fig. 47) bleaches out so that they turn blue. The down of a bustard is an extraordinary warm rust color which vanishes in sunlight as quickly as photo paper turns brown, leaving the down pale gray. As long as the down is covered by the feathers, this does not happen, whether the bird is alive or dead.

The salmon pink belly-feathers of an adult male common merganser bleach extremely quickly in light when the bird is dead, even though the lipochrome penetrates the horny part of the feather and is not merely on the surface. No matter how well you take care of these birds, they never get this pink color in captivity.

Once a feather has stopped growing it is dead, and the body cannot bring about any further changes in it. The old idea that a feather changes color because a new pigment is laid down is false: the color changes because the pigment becomes less dense. The cattle egret, however, is apparently an exception. It has rust-yellow feathers on the back and head, which are replaced by white ones when it molts. Slowly, a grainy brownish sediment forms in these feathers, perhaps through the action of light; this sediment gives them their color. This color, then, is produced by an increase in pigment in the dead feather.

Red, a lipochrome, turns out to be especially sensitive, disappearing in many birds when they are caged. After the molt it simply does not reappear. This is a nuisance not only in captive linnets, crossbills, and other finches but also in the North American tanagers, the South American scarlet ibis, and, up to a point, in the splendid North American cardinal. On the other hand, the color keeps its full beauty in several red South American tanagers, in red parrots, in the head-feathers of some of the South American cardinals (*Paroaria*).

Aviculturalists often have the idea that this fading is caused by a lack of sunlight and fresh air. They are wrong, for even if you put such birds in a big cage in the open where they are fully exposed to the weather their red color will disappear at the next molt, just as if they were kept in a small cage in a dim, stuffy room. In fact, light cannot have any influence on the color of a growing feather, for the feather sprouts in the dark covered by the old plumage. The real cause of fading is probably the lack of certain vitamins that are necessary to manufacture the pigments or, in the case of special breeding plumages, the failure to come into full breeding condition and produce the right sex hormones.

The marking of a single feather, its color and pattern, is designed so that, together with the neighboring feathers, it forms a particular decoration: these stripes or spots may either camouflage the bird or make it conspicuous, but they always have some special value. If, for instance, a part of the plumage is white with black bars, there need not be alternate rows of black and white feathers; the sharp boundary of the stripe can run across several feathers, which individually may be colored with an asymmetrical pattern of light and dark patches, different from feather to feather (Fig. 51*a* and *b*).

The head and neck of a mallard drake are iridescent green; he has a white collar not quite encircling his neck, and a chestnut breast. Looking more closely we see how this pattern is produced by the individual feathers. The head-feathers are pure iridescent green, then as we work downward, we find the same with white tips, then pure white feathers, then white ones with brown tips, and then all-brown ones. Only the part of each feather which shows is colored; toward the roots the feathers are the duller color of down.

The colors are distributed over the single feathers just as if someone had taken a white bird and painted it the way it looks. This makes us think that whatever the reason for a bird's being colored in a particular way, it is left to the single feathers, so to speak, to decide how to do it. How the needs of the animal are transferred into the individually meaningless pattern of each single feather is one of the great riddles of nature.

Birds that look like bark tend to have a very similar overall pattern, and on the same scale, regardless of how

big the individual feather is. The distance between the
bands of color is the same in large and small birds, so
that they give the same general impression of "barkiness."
This applies, of course, only to the parts of a bird you
can see when it is at rest (just as with many camouflaged
insects). When desert birds fold their wings they often
look the color of sand, while in flight the spread wings
and tail are a brilliant black and white, which may help
the birds to recognize others of their kind (Fig. 52).

Some young birds have a plumage that is essentially
the same as their parents'; this is especially true of those
species in which male and female look alike—garden

FIG. 51*a*. The rock dove, the
ancestor of the domestic pigeon. About one-sixth natural
size.

FIG. 51*b*. The right wing of a domestic
pigeon, colored like a rock dove. The
loose feathers shown beneath help to
form the black bands on the left wing.

FIG. 52. A stone curlew or thick-knee stretching himself. Notice the conspicuous markings on the wing, in contrast to the camouflaged upper parts.

warblers and graylag geese, for example. On the other hand, young male wild ducks and pheasants at first resemble their mothers and do not get their full male plumage until the first or second molt. The peacock does not get his full dress till he is three years old.

This is not to say that the different colors of the two sexes never show up until the birds are mature. In the eclectus parrot of New Guinea the males are green and the females red, and you can distinguish between the sexes in this way even when they are still nestlings.

A domestic hen whose ovaries are removed (called a poulard) changes to the male's plumage at the next molt, but a castrated male (called a capon) keeps his plumage unaltered. The female's plumage depends on her ovary producing what is called a sex hormone. If this hormone is injected into capons or poulards, they molt into the female plumage.

While the cock's plumage does not depend on a sex hormone, his handsome comb and wattles become smaller if he is castrated, and they can be restored by injections of male hormone.

In species such as the ruff, unlike the domestic fowl and other gallinaceous birds, it is the male breeding plumage which is dependent on sex hormone, for a castrated male cannot assume it again without injections.

But we cannot say that when the sexes are different, one or other plumage is the result of sex hormone; removal of the gonads of house sparrows does not affect the plumage of either sex, though it does prevent the male's beak from developing its usual blackish breeding color.

Where one sex is brightly colored and the other dull, it is usually true that the plainer parent—almost always the female—does most of the sitting on the eggs, for which she needs to be camouflaged when the nest is in the open. But if the female nests in a hole, as tits, woodpeckers, and shelduck do, she can afford to be as brightly colored as the male. Hole-nesting ducks can also allow themselves to have white down, while their relatives nesting in the open have to have a gray-brown, camouflaged down to cover their eggs (Figs. 14a and b). Figure 53 shows this very clearly, comparing the red-breasted merganser, which nests under bushes or boulders, with its close relative, the hole-nesting common merganser.

FIG. 53. On the left, a female common merganser; on the right, a female red-breasted merganser. Both birds have been plucked to show the down on one side of the breast only, that towards the edge of the picture. The common merganser, a hole-nester, has white down; the red-breasted merganser, which nests in the open, has dark down.

16. *Keeping Clean*

Feathers are very elaborate structures and need a great deal of care, far more than the hair of mammals. The oil glands that a human has all over his body are absent in birds—their secretion would just make the feathers sticky. Neither are there sweat glands, and in the heat birds cool off by panting like dogs (Fig. 37). But a bird does have a large gland at the base of its tail called the preen gland, which secretes a kind of oily fat. Sometimes special feathers grow out of it, acting like a wick to draw out the secretion.

To apply the oil a bird takes some of it on its bill (Fig. 54) and rubs it into the plumage. It also rubs its head first on the gland and then on its feathers, spreading the oil over its head, which the bird cannot reach with its beak. The passerines use their claws to distribute the oil that sticks to the beak and scratch it onto the head-feathers—an action which is so quick that you hardly notice its significance at all if you have not been warned.

The purpose of this oiling is to keep the feathers, and the bird inside them, from getting wet when the bird swims or when it rains. A bird usually oils itself after bathing, when the feathers often become sodden. You may have noticed that a caged bird which has not bathed for a long time gets much wetter than one which bathes regularly.

Some birds use powder to keep their feathers clean and waterproof. A few of them have special powder down areas in the feathers (Fig. 55); in others the growing feathers, especially the down, produce the powder. This

FIG. 54. A black stork gets oil from its preen gland. About one-thirteenth natural size.

FIG. 55. The lower back of an Australian frogmouth (a relative of the nightjars) with the feathers plucked. The huge bundles of powder down take the place of the preen gland. One-third natural size.

powder consists of tiny plates of horny material, less than a thousandth of an inch thick, which spread through the plumage.

You can see this powder when a heron or a pigeon bathes, for it forms a fine gray film on the water. The heron gets its powder from special powder-puffs out of sight on its breast, which it uses as other birds use their preen glands, rubbing its beak in them and then cleaning the feathers.

Birds that have a good supply of powder usually do not have much of a preen gland. Water birds always have a large gland, while ostriches, bustards, some parrots and pigeons, and a few other birds have none at all.

The majority of birds bathe in water. Some get right in it, others turn and twist about in the rain so that the water has a chance to penetrate their feathers (Fig. 56), and still others scuffle about in the wet grass and go through the motions of bathing. Desert birds and those of steppe country, including larks, gallinaceous birds, bustards, and sandgrouse, bathe only in the dust. Sparrows in anything, water, dust, or sand. The purpose of all this bathing must be not only to get clean, as it is for us, but also to remove parasites which attack the feathers of many species.

The way a bird bathes is instinctive, and so is the way it scratches its head with its claws. Each tends to be the same throughout any particular group of birds. There are two sorts of scratch: "over the wing" and "under the wing" (Figs. 57a and b); by watching for these one can sometimes tell whether or not certain birds are related. For instance, the Old World hornbills and the New World toucans look superficially alike—both have gigantic, sometimes very brightly colored beaks, and their general actions are very similar—but even without studying their anatomy we can tell that they belong to different groups from the way they scratch: toucans scratch under the wing, hornbills over it.

FIG. 56. A tame long-eared owl taking a bath in my shower.

FIG. 57*a*. A stork scratches itself "under the wing."

FIG. 57*b*. Sketch of a black-winged stilt scratching itself "over the wing."

All passerines and their relatives, as well as the true plovers, scratch over the wing. Almost all other birds, including pigeons, gallinaceous birds, storks and gulls, scratch the other way.

These examples show that the way a bird scratches itself is not connected with having long or short legs, or with the way it climbs a branch or stands on the ground, but rather with its ancestry.

Most birds shake themselves frequently. This shaking is instinctive, like scratching and bathing, and all the members of a species do it the same way from the beginning without being shown how. Some birds shake this way: first the body-feathers are ruffled up fairly evenly and slowly (Figs. 58*a* and *b*), and then the shake starts with the body and spreads up the neck to the head. In owls the shake travels just the opposite way. A bird shakes itself not only when it gets something on its feathers but at any time when the feathers are out of order. Disordered feathers seem to give an unpleasant sensation to the bird's skin, and the shake makes everything neat and comfortable again.

You can stop a bird shaking itself by giving it another stimulus. If you hold a shy bird in your hand for a while and then put it in a cage, it stays frightened for a long time with its feathers tightly compressed against its body.

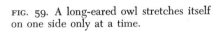

FIG. 58*a*. A penguin with its feathers laid flat, their normal position.
FIG. 58*b*. A penguin shaking itself, with its feathers all ruffled up.

FIG. 59. A long-eared owl stretches itself on one side only at a time.

After a time it begins to relax; and from the way the feathers alternately ruffle up and are flattened again, you can see it wants to shake but does not dare. Only when the bird is calm again does it complete the shake; then it does it again and again, until it has that wonderful feeling that its feathers are all in place. As a finishing touch it lifts itself half erect and makes a couple of quick wing-flaps, usually ending with an audible snap. Then the wings are again folded away under the covering feathers.

Birds also stretch themselves, but unlike mammals they usually do this on one side at a time, holding the other side in its resting position. The wing and corresponding leg are stretched backward and downward and the tail is fanned out on the same side (Figs. 59 and 52). Most birds also have another way of stretching in which both wings are lifted, often without being properly opened, and the neck stretched forward (Fig. 60). Some birds such as doves spread their tails symmetrically at the same time.

FIG. 60. A little bittern stretches its wing upward and its head forward.

17. *Eating Habits*

There is a basic difference between the way mammals eat and the way birds eat. Most mammals have teeth that can grind up plant food, and very few of them can swallow large objects whole. Even the carnivorous mammals cut up their meat with their scissor-like teeth. Instead of teeth birds have horny shears which bite on each other; these shears are modified in geese to form a row of fine teeth and in parrots to make a kind of rasp.

A few birds hold their food in their feet and bite off small pieces. Owls, parrots, many but not all raptors, and, of special interest, the European purple gallinule, a kind of rail—all these clutch nuts, fruit, or meat in one foot and raise it to the beak, which is often bent down a little way toward the foot (Fig. 3).

Other birds are more awkward about it. A northern shrike clenches its prey in one foot, holding its leg in a peculiar way with the tarsus resting on the perch, and bends over to tear bits off (Fig. 61). The bearded tit does the same (Fig. 62). Most often, when the feet are used, the food is clamped under them and the bird tears off with its beak what it can swallow. Ravens and raptors do it like this. Birds sometimes use this method to dig the kernel out of a seed. A bird holds its food in this way long before it can feed itself and without any example to copy. Species that do not hold their food in this way never learn to imitate it from others. A gallinaceous bird or a pigeon has a terrible time worrying a piece of lettuce or bread-crust until it can shake off a piece small enough

FIG. 61. A northern shrike holding a mouse in its foot with its tarsus resting on the perch.

FIG. 62. A coal tit pecks off a bite of the food clamped under its foot.

to swallow, and it never occurs to the bird to stand on the food and peck pieces off it. The brushturkey is an exception; for although it is a gallinaceous bird, it holds snails under its foot to eat them.

Most birds tend to gulp down large pieces of food, leaving it to their gizzards to grind them up. Here are some examples of how different species deal with their food. A pigeon swallows peas whole; the peas are then softened but not digested in the capacious crop, which is a pouch in the throat. The peas then go to the first, glandular part of the stomach, which releases digestive juices, and next to the muscular stomach, the gizzard. Here the peas are ground up by being rubbed between horny, ridged plates lining the gizzard, sometimes helped by a little grit which is found there. The food, which is now a kind of mush, leaves the stomach and is further decomposed in the intestine so that sugar, fat and proteins can pass through the gut-wall and enter the body dissolved in the blood.

The "toothed" beaks of geese, helped by powerful jaw muscles, cut up the grass they eat. Otherwise both geese and domestic chickens deal with food very much like the pigeons; geese and chickens, however, have a pair of large blind tubes, called caeca (singular: caecum), opening off the intestine, of which the pigeons have only vestiges. The purpose of a caecum is to digest the cellulose in plant food; as one might expect, birds that eat mainly plants usually have larger caeca than insect- or meat-eaters, though the pigeons are exceptional. Many mammals have a large caecum (only one) which is also concerned with digesting plant food; in humans the caecum has degenerated into the small but notorious appendix.

A lot of people think that all birds have crops; this is not true. On the contrary, only a few special kinds of birds have developed or need this storage pouch in their throats. The best known examples are the pigeons, the gallinaceous birds, the parrots, and the raptors. These birds eat food which is either hard to digest, like seeds, or, in the birds of prey, too much for the stomach to hold all at once. The crop stores the food until the stomach is ready for it. A peregrine falcon, for instance, makes the most of its kill by tearing the flesh from the bones and stuffing its ample crop, which is soon emptied again by the quick action of the stomach.

Many seed-eating songbirds and some fish-eaters have no proper crop but only a widening of the throat which they can fill with food. The same is true of ducks, geese, and cranes. Old World flycatchers, robins, and Old World warblers, all of which feed on small insects, have no crops.

Some grazing birds like ostriches have a small pocket just behind the base of the tongue. When they take a mouthful of grass or leaves, they clip it off straight into this pocket. When the pocket is full the bird raises its head and we see the lump of food sliding lazily down the long neck to the stomach. Mammals quickly squirt their food down the throat to the stomach and seem to find it unpleasant if a piece of it gets stuck on the way. Birds are exactly the opposite: they swallow slowly. A tern seems quite unconcerned if its stomach is digesting the head of a big fish while the tail is still sticking out of its mouth.

Unlike mammals, there are few birds that eat only grass and leaves. These bird vegetarians eat tender leaves, buds (the bullfinch is notorious for this), and especially seeds, which finches dehusk with their beaks and other birds swallow whole. Berry-eaters are particularly common in the tropics where there are berries all the year—often specially colored so that birds can recognize them from a distance.

It is in the plant's interest, of course, that the bird does not damage the seed when it eats the fruit but passes it out unharmed with the droppings or coughs it up as a pellet; this is how the plant spreads. But some birds mar the prospects of the tree they perch in by destroying the seed. The hawfinch cracks a cherrystone and throws away the fruit; the bullfinch does the same with a rowan berry.

Still more interesting are two species of large pigeons which live in and around New Guinea. Both eat the same fruit but live off different parts of it. In the virgin forests stand tall trees with a fruit which in size and shape resembles an unshelled green walnut. When this fruit is ripe, the large fruit-pigeons (*Ducula*) arrive and swallow them whole; in the droppings you can find the big, shiny, hard-shelled seeds, which only an axe can split. In this way the birds help to propagate the tree. These pigeons have a fairly thin stomach wall and a very wide intestine, and digest only the juicy flesh of the fruit while the big stone passes unharmed through the gut. Not so the Nicobar pigeon, which eats the same fruit but deals with it the other way round. It also swallows the food whole, but its powerful gizzard breaks up the stone and the kernel is digested. What is left passes out in pieces through the relatively narrow gut. Because it does not have to live off the watery, spongy flesh, this species needs fewer fruits than the other.

In birds, as in mammals, the eaters of meat have an intestine which is rough-walled and narrow, but the stomach has no special equipment such as the stomach muscles of plant-eating birds or the four-fold stomach of horses and cows. Although bustards and ostriches eat grass and herbs, they do not have the horny grinding plates in the gizzard which usually go with such a diet; the food in the muscular stomach is ground up by grit. The small intestine digests some things; but the main work, the digestion of cellulose from plants, is the work of the two caeca, which are as magnificently developed in these birds as in the horse, the rabbit, or the guinea pig. Many gallinaceous birds, such as the capercaillie and ptarmigan which live in winter on pine needles and the tips of twigs, have large caeca; these birds also have a well-developed muscular gizzard which begins the task of breaking down the food.

A lot of birds collect the indigestible parts of their food in the stomach and from time to time cough them out as "pellets." Owls swallow fairly large animals whole, and throw up the hair, feathers, and all the bones rolled up together. It is remarkable that an owl can digest all the muscle fibers and ligaments without even beginning to eat away the bones; the delicate ribs of mice are quite undamaged in the pellets, and the skulls have been so cleaned out that they can be incorporated straight away into a museum collection.

The raptors which hunt by day do not normally produce pellets. A goshawk or a falcon picks its prey clean, tearing the meat from the larger bones, and so avoids eating hair or feathers except what little sticks to the meat. What small bones it takes are dissolved by hydrochloric acid in the stomach, along with the rest of the food. The real expert at digesting bones is the bearded vulture, whose stomach is so acid it can dissolve the whole of a cow's vertebra.

Birds that eat only insects get rid of the horny, chitinous hard parts in the form of pellets. The European kingfisher does the same with the bones and scales of fish it has swallowed. Herons, gulls, and pelicans, on the other hand, digest this hard material or pass it out through the gut.

Animals can always digest meat and animal food in general more easily then cellulose from plants. So, most seed-eating birds feed their small young with insects and worms. This diet is also better than plant food in providing the chicks with the protein they need for growing. Young gallinaceous birds and most young waterfowl, as well as bustards and cranes, also start out on animal food and then change to their adult diet mainly of plants. We have seen also that the grain-eating pigeons feed their young on crop-milk, which is really a homemade animal food.

18. *How Birds Communicate with Each Other*

The so-called sound- and sign-languages of birds are expressions of excitement, but we must assume they have some purpose, either for the bird which utters them or for its companions—they must help the species to survive. We can see that birds take notice of the calls of a companion and often act in response to them, but we must distinguish between what a bird does communicate and what it intends to communicate. There is no reason to believe that a bird intends to communicate anything by its calls, for a young bird which has been brought up by human beings and has never seen or heard its own kind utters the same sounds in the same situations as if it were wild; it apparently has no idea what the sounds are for. Nevertheless, when there are other birds present, the outburst of excitement communicates something to them.

We ourselves become sad when we are with sad people and laugh and are happy when we are with gay people; but this does not mean that our sad or happy friends intend us to be the way they are. A call such as the alarm call may seem intended to warn a bird's mate or its offspring, because it is uttered with special vehemence when they are around. But we can interpret it more simply by supposing that a pair of birds are themselves more fearful and easily alarmed when they are with their young and that their excitement finds expression in louder calls.

If we use the word "language" in talking of birds, it is not to be taken in the human sense; we are born with the ability to learn a language but not with the language itself. The means of expression of birds are inherited and, with a very few exceptions, cannot be changed. Animal language is more like our laughing and crying than our speech.

Some birds are completely dumb; certain New World vultures are an example. A lot of birds which, like the European cuckoo, live alone except during the mating season, have but one call which they use only at this time to attract a mate. On the other hand, birds that live together in families or flocks usually have a whole range of sounds or expressive actions. This is what you would expect, for birds that are not sociable do not have the opportunity or the need to communicate.

In some species the male, female, and young have different voices; even when we cannot distinguish at all between the voices some birds can by hearing them recognize their mates or certain other individuals from others of their kind. Tame geese can recognize the voice of their keeper without seeing him, even when he is talking with other humans. The way parrots learn to speak and some passerines to imitate songs shows that despite differences between the structure of their ear and ours, they hear sounds exactly as we do.

To explain the meaning of the calls of birds, it will be simplest to take a couple of well-known birds as examples. First the domestic fowl. Everyone has heard a cock crow; all he wants to say—instinctively, of course—is "Here is a cock!" The call attracts a hen, but for the cock's rival it is a sign that the place is taken already and that he must either start a fight or go away.

This cry is not an invitation to the hen to copulate, for like many kinds of display it has nothing to do with mounting. When a cock is really making advances to a hen, he circles her in a peculiar way called waltzing, drooping the wing that is away from her, uttering a deep "Gogerogog." If the lady is willing, she crouches without a word and lets him mount her. When it is all over she gets up, shakes herself, and trips away.

Chickens do not have a general "contact call" for summoning others but special calls for special situations. The broody hen's "cluck" is only for her children; a rooster that has found something to eat calls, "Tik tik tik," until his harem runs up and one of them takes the food. When members of a flock are separated, they have no way of calling one another together again, as ducks and geese have.

To warn of danger chickens have two distinct calls. If a strange man or a dog enters the farmyard, they call, "Gogogogock," which is the warning of danger on the ground and means to the wild jungle-fowl, "Into a tree!" But if a bird flies swiftly over the chicken-run, we hear a long, drawn-out, husky "Rehh," which means, "Danger overhead, take cover!" The European blackbird's "Chuk-chuk-chuk-chuk" means danger on the ground, and a repeated long, drawn-out "Seeee," a flying enemy. When chickens are alarmed or are being pursued, they repeat the ground alarm cry, only louder, and keep it up long after the coast is clear. In such circumstances it sounds exactly like the cackling of a hen which has laid an egg, and other hens often join in the chorus.

This cackling is a mystery, for every other bird keeps as quiet as possible near its clutch so as not to betray the hidden nest. Chickens do exactly the opposite. In general, domestic animals use their voices much more than the corresponding wild forms, for whom every call increases the danger of discovery. It may be that the expression of the mother hen's fear when she leaves her nesting place is not inhibited in the domestic bird as it is in the wild and finds expression in this alarm cry. If this is true, what most people take as a cry of joy is really a cry of fright. I once noticed that a hybrid red jungle-fowl hen which was laying her eggs in an out-of-the-way spot would slip away from the nest before cackling.

There is another remarkable kind of cackling, which is heard only from hens that are waiting for something: for instance, when the nest they want to lay in is already occupied, or when the man with their food is late. This drawn-out sound is impossible to describe although you can imitate it fairly easily. Wild jungle-fowl seem to have it too, in a rudimentary form, but one cannot imagine what use it would be in the wild.

If you hold a cock or a hen and frighten it, it will utter a loud cry of fear, which sometimes brings exceptionally brave cocks to protect their wives or families. Many songbirds, raptors, and parrots have a similar cry when they have been caught, and we naturally want to know what it means. First, the cry calls the attention of the whole neighborhood to the attacker and in many birds, especially those with parents in attendance, it is a cry for help that may cause the attacker to be mobbed. Second, the call may be of use even to birds that cannot count on help from others, for it is unusually shrill and painful to our ears and in a way must be frightening to an enemy.

Everybody has heard baby chickens peep, and you can sometimes hear them when they are still in the egg. If the peeping of a live chick is soft, it expresses contentment, and the mother knows, humanly speaking, that all is well. When the peep is loud and strong, it means discomfort or fear, and the mother tries to get to her chick as long as she hears its despairing call. It can happen that a clumsy mother will step on one of her children, which of course sets up a great wail. The hen keeps looking around for danger, without noticing that she herself is the cause of the trouble.

For the second example of the meaning of bird language let us consider the graylag goose, the ancestor of the domestic goose. As we have mentioned, a pair of wild graylags are extremely faithful to each other and usually stay together all their lives. Between breeding seasons they live in a close family group with their last lot of young. Such strong family ties call for a means of communication, and many of us know the ringing "Gagangak" of the mother and father calling the family together. They can tell each other's voices among those of hundreds of their kind. Graylag goslings that have been hatched by a hen or in an incubator do not recognize this call of their species; they are scared to death the first time they hear it and have to get used to it gradually. This does not mean, however, that the goose has to learn to make this cry; at the right age it makes the sound just like its parents, even if it has never heard it from another bird.

A short, clipped "Honk" is the gander's alarm call. When the mother hears it, she enters the water at once with her family. Parents and children alike, when they have driven off an enemy, give themselves the treat of the so-called triumph ceremony, which does much to strengthen the family ties. Young ganders that approach another family to inspect their intended brides often pretend to drive away an enemy and then lift up this loud cry of triumph.

When the family has been resting and wants to move on, the birds utter certain soft calls which signal the departure and keep the flock informed that everyone is present. In flight the same calls are used to keep the birds in touch with each other. As the flock gets ready to fly, the calls become louder and more frequent, and geese have a peculiar sideways shake of the head which always precedes the take-off.

You have probably seen an angry goose defending her young (Fig. 32), hissing loudly with neck stretched out and beak open wide, every now and then ruffling up her feathers and shaking them noisily. This is a gesture of threat which any enemy—goose or not—will understand.

FIG. 63. Windpipes of the goldeneye. *a* The female's, *b* The male's when he is at rest (seen from behind), *c* The male's when his neck is bent backward, as in display (see Fig. 64).

Young geese that have passed the peeping stage have a peculiar cry of distress when they are lost. Another call of this species is a yearning, melancholy lament repeated again and again in the twilight hours of dawn by a goose whose husband has deserted her.

Totally different from the geese in their breeding behavior are the mallards and their descendants, the domestic ducks. They, too, have a language of sounds and signs, but it is quite different from that of the geese. This difference corresponds to the mallard's very different habits of mating and raising its young (see Chapter 12).

Just as the drake's plumage is different in most ducks from his wife's, so is his voice, and he even has a special sound-producing organ. The female's windpipe branches at its lower end in the usual way for a bird (Fig. 63*a*), but at this fork the drake has a large bony drum (Figs. 63*b* and *c*) whose shape varies in different species. Male domestic ducks and mallards have as their usual call a low, somewhat burring "Raeb," which can express fear or anger or can be used to attract another bird, depending on how it is uttered. During the courtship of autumn and winter the drakes utter a high piping whistle which is produced with the help of the bony drum in the windpipe. As it utters this sound, the bird stands up in the water, almost touching his breast with his beak, so that the drum is stretched (Fig. 63c). In other species also, drakes producing these male calls make certain movements to shorten or lengthen their windpipes; these movements contort the windpipe into curious shapes (Fig. 64).

During the autumn and winter we hear the familiar "Quack quak quakquak" of female mallard and domestic ducks, but these females are wisely silent in the spring when there are wanton males about. But if one shows up, the female eggs her husband on to attack it, pointing to it with her bill over her shoulder and calling, "Quegeg geg queg queg."

When a duck is afraid, we hear a long "Quek quek," accompanied by an upward tilting of the beak, as if the bird were preparing to spring in the air. Species that usually perch in trees do not make an upward movement but point more horizontally, moving their heads backwards and forwards as chickens and pigeons do when they walk.

The mother leads her ducklings about, calling a soft "quark." If you imitate the sound well enough, you can get young ducks to come to you, provided they have not been led around by a real mother duck.

The voices of young birds, like those of young humans, are often shriller than their parents'. The young bustard normally produces a soft tremulo; but when it gets lost,

FIG. 64. Drake goldeneye. 1. At rest. 2. Getting ready to call. 3. Calling.

it emits a sad, long, drawn-out piping, rather like the voice of a peacock chick; after a time the sound can really get on your nerves. But the adult bustard has no voice to speak of, beyond a few groans and snorts.

As a young bird grows up, its voice may break, depending on its species. Gulls and many others keep their juvenile tone long after they can make the adult calls. The wonderful "Coo-eee" of the adult European curlew can be heard from the chick still in the egg, although, of course, it sounds thinner and weaker. Even when they are adult, birds like the European curlew do not make deep sounds like the raucous ducks, and so their voices never break.

For young birds that are fed in the nest the amount of noise they make there varies from species to species, according to the need for concealment. Young hooded crows are amazingly silent in the nest, but young rooks make a deafening noise. Since rooks nest in colonies and do not have to be discreet to avoid betraying the nest, they can give free rein to their emotions, which the solitary hooded crows cannot afford to do. Young ravens are also very noisy in the nest; since the adults are both courageous and well armed, they have no real enemies except man, who has arrived so lately on the scene that the adjustments of natural selection have not had time to take him into account. Solitary-nesting species are usually quite silent in the nest until the moment their food is brought; as soon as they leave the nest, all this changes. Young greenfinches which have just left the nest keep reminding their parents where they are by endlessly repeating, "Choo-eee." Hole-nesters are usually much noisier in the nest, and young woodpeckers and rollers clamor without interruption. Being safe in their holes they need not worry about drawing attention to themselves.

Young megapodes are independent from birth. They never meet their parents and do not live in flocks, and,

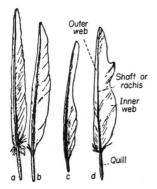

FIG. 65. *a* First primary (noise feather) of the adult male golden-eye. *b* The same feather in the female. *c* The noise feather of the male common scoter, and *d* of the Indian tree-duck. (The parts of the feather are indicated in *d.*)

as a result, they have no voice at all—there is never any-one for them to say anything to.

The sounds birds use to communicate with each other are not always made with their voices. Woodpeckers pro-duce a far-carrying drumming sound by tapping their beaks quickly on a dead branch, and rivals use this sound to challenge each other just as European robins use their songs.

Other birds produce sounds by means of specially shaped feathers, usually sharply tapered primary feath-ers on the wing (Fig. 65). The apt German name for the goldeneye is "bell duck," for the adult male in flight makes a bell-like whistle with his slender outer primaries, which is unlike the sound of any other duck. The male common scoter makes an even louder sound, and the Australian crested pigeon produces a noise with the third primary. (When this feather is missing in each wing during the molt, there is no whistle).

The inconspicuously colored Indian tree-duck makes a loud whistle by means of a special lobe on the inner web of the outermost primary (Fig. 65). The other tree-ducks, which lack this lobe, do not have the same whistling flight, but they are distinguished from each other by conspicuous wing patterns and flight calls. For all such sociable birds that fly at dusk, it is important that they be able to recognize their own kind, whether by color or the sound of their wings.

A comparison of the mute swan and the whooper shows how birds may use two completely different sounds for the same purpose. The whooper's windpipe describes a long loop inside the hollow breastbone (Fig. 66); it is gifted with a great voice, as its name says, and migrating birds trumpet to each other to keep in touch. The mute swan is nearly but not quite as silent as its name implies; instead of the long, resonating tube of the whooper its windpipe runs straight from the base of the tongue to the lungs. But if its voice is small, the bird makes up for it in another way; for the whistle of its wings in flight can be heard several hundred yards away—a sound that is quite astonishing when you first hear it. We still do not know how this sound is produced, for there are no specially shaped feathers and the wingbeat is apparently the same as the whooper's, which makes no appreciable noise.

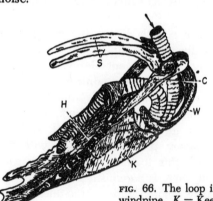

FIG. 66. The loop in the whooper swan's windpipe. $K =$ Keel of the breastbone, $C =$ Coracoid bone, $W =$ Wishbone (Furcula), $S =$ Shoulder blade, $H =$ Windpipe running in hollowed-out keel of breastbone.

FIG. 67. The tail of the East Siberian pintail snipe. The outer strip-like feathers produce a sound during the display flight.

Tail-feathers can also make sounds. The common snipe as it circles high over its nesting area will every now and then make a slanting dive that lasts two or three seconds. As it descends, it spreads out the tail and wings, which are set fluttering and produce a weird, quavering "huhu-huhuhu," called bleating or drumming. Many a person walking in the marshes in the spring and early summer has been puzzled by this strange music, and it may well have given rise to some eerie legends. The sound is produced by vibrations of the outer tail-feathers, which are narrower than the inner ones; and the fluttering of the wings modulates the tone to produce the vibrant effect. In the pintail snipe of Siberia the outer tail-feathers have so developed that the sound they make is even louder. (Fig. 67).

Many birds (as well as mammals, including humans) utter sounds and use other forms of expression that do not seem to have a single meaning but express a general excitement. Cranes trumpet (Fig. 68) and storks clatter their beaks (Fig. 69) both when they are angry and when they greet their mates, and many other birds do the same things in these two situations. Perhaps anger and greeting are not such different things for these birds. We humans weep to express a wide range of emotions, from sadness to great joy.

FIG. 68. A crane trumpeting.

FIG. 69. Stork parents on the nest clattering their beaks.

The sign language of animals usually consists of symbolic actions which tells their companions how they feel. An angry heron makes itself large, ruffling the feathers and drawing in its head and neck ready to attack. If it wants to be friendly, it lays the feathers flat and stretches its neck straight upwards, as much as to say, "See, I can't hurt you."

When a mute swan threatens an enemy, it raises its wings by lifting the elbows, swells its neck and draws back its head (Figs. 70 and 19). This attitude strikes fear not only into swans but into any opponent. When two mated mute swans swim towards each other in a friendly way they must show their feeling in their action. Their wings are laid flat, and the neck is not swollen, but is held straight upright (Fig. 71). A display of un-warlike behavior thus means affection. Darwin, in his book *The Expression of the Emotions in Man and Animals*, described something like this in the way horses hold their ears. When soldiers present arms they are going through the ritual of holding out their weapons, originally a token of friendship.

It must be added that closely related species may have very different ways of expressing themselves. Compare, for instance, the way a mute swan and a black-necked swan act when they are angry (Figs. 70 and 72).

It is peculiar to watch a young bird that has been brought up by itself the first time it hears the voice of one of its species: it is startled by calls which it may itself

FIG. 70. Angry mute swan.

FIG. 71. Friendly mute swans.

FIG. 72. A black-necked swan attacking.

have uttered hundreds of times. Obviously, it does not know how it sounds. I once brought up a corncrake from the egg, keeping him in the house. By the next spring his voice was so loud and harsh in the confined room that unsuspecting visitors greeted by this continual hoarse cry of "Rarrp rarrp" used to back away in fright. At the beginning of May I brought in one of the corncrake's brothers, which had been given away in the autumn. They paid little attention to one another at first; but the next morning when the newcomer started to croak, our bird was terribly scared and rushed to hide in a corner. He showed no anger or jealousy of the new bird, however, and gradually became used to his companion's call.

Some people wonder which birds sing and to what purpose. Of the 9000 or so species of birds about 4000 belong to the true songbirds (or Oscines), which comprise most of the passerines. These birds have special membranes and muscle fibres around the place where the windpipe branches to each lung. The fibres, which are better developed in males than in females, are able to modify the sounds the bird utters; but the system of producing sound is much more complicated than a mere blowing out of air to produce a particular noise.

Apart from the parrots, only passerines can imitate a strange sound. A duck brought up in a chicken-run never learns to crow—it can only make the sounds appropriate to its kind.

At the beginning of the breeding season most male passerines produce what people call song—that is to say, a series of more or less pleasant sounds. One thinks of the nightingale, skylark, song thrush, or European blackbird, whose songs give pleasure to our ears, for we think of song as something beautiful. But if you judge simply by the excellence of the sounds, you will have to admit that a plover showing off to his female has more of a song than a chirping sparrow, which is one of the "real song-birds." By no means all songbirds sing beautifully, and there are many other sounds—the cooing of pigeons, the crowing of a cock, the purring of a nightjar, the call of the European cuckoo, and the roaring of a stag—which are sometimes not regarded as songs in the narrow sense but which serve the same purpose, to mark out a territory and attract a mate.

It has been shown that most of the true songbirds can imitate strange sounds even though they have only simple songs themselves. Some of them learn their own songs by imitation, others do not. The song of the chiffchaff and grasshopper warbler is innate, as I found by raising them indoors. Even some of the birds with a very elaborate song can produce it without ever hearing it from others —European blackbirds and song thrushes, for example. In the autumn a young hand-reared song thrush weaves into his own practicing all sorts of sounds he has heard from other birds, and the result is a stream of warbling gibberish. But when spring comes, he produces distinct phrases which are quite recognizably thrush—though perhaps not very good thrush—and in which the borrowed sounds are arranged into thrush rhythms.

Chaffinches learn rather more of their song. Without any examples to listen to, they produce a song which sounds very unlike a wild chaffinch's but has some of the same rhythm. Normal chaffinches differ individually in the details of their songs; these details they learn from their neighbors in their first spring. One may say that they are handed on by tradition from generation to generation.

We have to distinguish between birds brought up entirely alone and birds that have been able to hear other species or any kind of sounds which they can imitate. If they can hear other sounds, they may develop their own songs or they may borrow from what they have heard. Bird-fanciers sometimes make use of the imitating ability of young male bullfinches, European blackbirds, starlings, and various exotic species when they are starting to sing, by whistling songs to them which the birds can imitate very closely. Some trained birds completely renounce their own song in favor of what they have learned, while others acquire the song of their own species as soon as they hear it.

Even in the wild many birds weave snatches of other songs into their own. This has sometimes been called "mocking," as if the bird were trying to make fun of its teacher. The American mockingbirds are famous for this, and so are the red-backed shrike, the bluethroat, the icterine warbler, the starling, the shamah, and others.

Most of these birds have a song that is clumsy enough already, and they toss in the extra sounds rather meaninglessly, though almost always in the same order. It seems quite possible that a mimic which imitates a partridge or crow or golden oriole has never heard the bird itself but has simply picked up the calls at second-hand from the songs of others.

Birds that are cleverer connect people or places more closely with the sounds they imitate; starlings, crows, and certain kinds of parrots can make this sort of association. This ability gives their calls the air of being like human language, but they are not quite the same. My hand-reared young budgerigar, for instance, makes a gurgling sound whenever I pick up a bottle, and as soon as a bee-eater flies into the room, he imitates the visitor's loud "Pitt pitt" cry. But even when birds acquire these sounds they seem unable to manipulate them in the way that is an essential feature of real language. All the same, one gets rather a shock when one knocks on a door and hears a parrot say "Come in." Of course, the words and the knock are simply two sounds that the bird has often heard together and has learned to connect.

Wild parrots have never been known to mimic sounds; it seems that only the boredom of captivity awakes the urge. Once it is awakened, however, the urge can become so great that whenever you speak or whistle, the bird comes up to you, ruffling up its ear-coverts, and listens closely to what you say; sometimes it practices the sounds afterwards.

When we think about it, it is remarkable that songbirds and parrots are the only animals, apart from humans, that can make sounds other than those they are born to make. Even the apes, which are so closely related to us, cannot do anything like this, although if you talk to one it watches your mouth attentively and looks as if any moment it were going to reply.

19. *Birds' Senses*

Smell

Smell is not as important to birds as it is to most mammals, even to humans. You can tell this from the fact that the nostrils are not at the tip of a bird's beak (except in the kiwi) and that birds do not sniff.

Many birds of prey are able to smell, but they seem to smell things only when they hold them in their beaks; from the beak the odor particles pass via the mouth to the organs of smell located in the nasal passages between the mouth and the nostrils. It is easy to show, for instance, that ravens and Old World vultures do not find their prey by smell. If you cover a piece of meat, these birds cannot find it, whereas a dog in the same situation would go straight to it. It is clear that the sense of smell of most birds is far too poor to be used to recognize their nest holes, their mates and children, or, if they are tame birds, their keepers. The only birds which seem at all likely to have a good sense of smell are the New World vultures, many petrels, and, above all, the New Zealand kiwi, which has poor eyesight but is active at night and has large organs of smell.

Taste

A bird can definitely taste what it eats. Taste-buds are scattered over the salivary glands toward the back of the tongue, in the mucous membrane under the tongue, and especially on the soft palate and at the entrance to the gullet. A bird, therefore, does not taste food in its beak or with the tip of its tongue but only with the rear parts of its mouth.

Sensitivity to the four sorts of taste, sweet, sour, bitter, and salty, varies with the species. Seed-eaters, for instance, are not very sensitive to bitter things, probably because their natural food is very bitter. I have dipped pieces of bread in quinine and given them to parrots and other birds without their showing the slightest offense at the acrid taste. Other people found the same thing true when they fed seed-eaters and titmice seeds soaked in picric acid. These species generally like sweet things, and they can taste sweetness in about the same dilution as we can. Geese and ducks, on the other hand, either cannot taste sweetness or do not like it, for if you give them a piece of sugar they may take it out of curiosity, or when they are expecting food from you, but they will drop it again. On the other hand, canaries and parrots love sweet things.

Taste matters to fruit-eaters, but to other birds it is less important than it is to us; most of them bolt their food whole without chewing it up. Remember that an owl swallows a mouse whole and that most thrushes do the same with rowan berries. Fish-eaters eat whole fish, and chickens and pigeons swallow grain and peas without biting them up. In deciding what is food, birds like these go by the shape of an object, how hard it is, and, if they have seen it before, by its color.

Touch

The sense of touch is highly developed in birds. They immediately notice and dislike the slightest touch on their feathers. The quills of the feathers act as long levers to tell the skin if anything moves them. Some birds also have bristles or whiskers around the mouth that can be raised to examine food or other things: owls, which can hardly see at close quarters, have very large bristles.

There are special nerve-endings in woodpeckers' tongues, in the beak-flanges of certain nestlings, and on the soft beaks of waders and waterfowl. People often

FIG. 73. A snipe probing for its food.

claim that snipes and ducks use these organs not only to feel but also to sense chemical stimuli and odors that we cannot perceive: for instance, to find water or hidden food, or perceive that an enemy is approaching. I have never been able to convince myself that this is true. The snipe hunting for worms (Fig. 73) certainly does not smell the worm from above ground; it sticks its beak into the mud at random and, if it feels a worm, grabs it. I have also noticed that half-tame mallards living free only know that a man or a dog is dangerously near when they see or hear him. The duck's magnificent eyesight and sensitive beak make it unnecessary for us to assume it has some unknown sense to help it find food under water.

Sight

Almost all birds have extremely good eyesight, better than any other animals, and for this reason the bird's eye has been the subject of much study. Most birds, like humans and many apes and monkeys, depend mainly on their eyes and ears to know what is going on around them.

A bird's eye is almost always very large; it is different from ours in many ways. In the retina, the light-sensitive part of the eye, vision is sharpest in a small area called the yellow spot or fovea (plural: foveae). In a ten-millionth of a square inch in this region our eyes have about ten light-sensitive cells, while a European buzzard's has about sixty-five. The European buzzard's eye can distinguish detail two or three times as fine as we can.

It is amazing what sharp-sighted birds can see. They can pick out another bird that is flying so high it is almost invisible to us, even when they see it flying against the sun. They can also spot things on the ground you would never notice. If you walk down a gravel path with a tame raven on your arm, he may suddenly fly down to the ground some yards away and come back with a microscopic crumb of bread he has seen in the gravel. But even the sharpest-eyed birds are sometimes not able to distinguish objects that keep still. A jackdaw will never spot a grasshopper unless it moves, and a goshawk will overlook a crouching partridge.

Birds, like mammals, are able to focus on both near and far objects. The amount a bird has to change its focus (or accommodate, as it is called) depends not only on the distance but also on whether the object is in air or water. European cormorants and other birds that have to be able to see both underwater, in order to fish, and above water, have astonishing powers of accommodation, four or five times as great as man's. Not all birds do so well. Chickens and pigeons accommodate slightly less well than man. Owls are far worse and seem unable to see anything close to them. If you throw a mealworm to a tame scops owl, it pounces on it at once; but if the food should slip out of its talons, the owl has to stand back a little until it can focus its eyes on the food and grab it again. Large owls when they eat a rat or a mouse lift it parrotwise to their beaks, then close their eyes and use their whiskers to find the head, which they swallow first.

In front of the light-sensitive nerve endings of the retina of birds (and reptiles) there are small drops of oil. These oil drops are usually reddish or yellowish but in nocturnal birds tend to be colorless or bluish. A yellow filter would seem to be useful to a bird (as it is to photographers) when he wants to see through hazy air. On the other hand, yellow and red filter out some of the blue and green light rays, so the bird will tend to see everything rather reddish. In some species this red-vision is toned down by colorless oil drops which lie between the reddish ones.

People usually underestimate how mobile a bird's eyes are, for the eyeball moves differently from ours, more like a reptile's. We move the eyeball back and forth, rotating it inside the eye-opening with its eyelid, but a bird's eye-opening moves with the eyeball; in other words, its pupil always stays in the middle, whether it looks backward or forward, up or down (Figs. 74*a* and *b*). Like reptiles, birds can move each eye independently; one eye

FIG. 74*a*. A red kite looks sideways.

FIG. 74*b*. A lesser spotted eagle looks straight ahead.

FIG. 75. A long-eared owl looks sideways and downward.

FIG. 76. A barn owl looks directly behind itself, its beak over the middle of the back.

can look up and behind while the other is directed forward and down. We can see this most easily in birds like the African ground hornbill which have long eyelash-feathers.

Owls' eyes are quite fixed in their heads, so despite what people say they cannot roll their eyes. Each eye, instead of being round, is tube-shaped, and the two of them sit in their gigantic sockets like a pair of little field glasses. The sockets, which take up a large part of the head, are so big that in comparison with them the owl's brain looks like an afterthought. When an owl is disturbed, it has to turn its whole head around to see what is the matter (Figs. 75 and 76). This gives it a somewhat droll expression, especially since its eyes do not look to the side as most birds' do, but obliquely forward.

Owls' eyes resemble ours in that they both look in the same direction, but for many birds each eye has its own field of vision. Many birds, when they want to examine a strange object, look at it with one eye sideways, rather than directly as we would. When a bird examines an object with one eye sideways it uses a certain part of the retina; another part is called into play when the bird uses both eyes directly. Birds that examine objects in both ways tend to have two foveae for detailed vision in each of these regions. Owls, like us, have only one fovea in each eye.

We close our eyes, as most mammals do, by dropping the upper eyelid. Birds and reptiles almost always do it the other way, raising the lower lid. Birds also have a well developed "nictitating membrane"—a thin third eyelid of which we have only a trace—which can be pulled over the surface of the eye. This membrane, as well as the eyelids, often moves independently in each eye. Owls are an exception: they usually blink by lowering the upper lid, which makes them look astonishingly human; but when they sleep, they raise the lower lids.

The iris of the eye of birds and reptiles has striated muscle, which works much faster than the smooth muscle in our irises and those of other mammals. As a result the bird's pupil constricts at lightning speed when the light brightens and widens as rapidly as when it fades. In addition, the eyes are, in this respect, independent of one

FIG. 77. A snowy owl with the light coming from the side. The left eye, which is in the light, is less open and has a smaller pupil than the right eye which is in shadow.

another, so that when one eye is in shadow, it has a wider pupil than the one that is in the light (Fig. 77).

The iris is usually dark, but in some very different birds it is quite colorful. The color may vary with the bird's age and sex. The male and female of the black-necked stork, for instance, look alike except for the iris of their eyes, which is brilliant yellow in the female and dark brown in the male. The iris of male wood ducks, bee-eaters, and a type of ibis is a splendid ruby-red; in the adult European cormorant it is emerald-green and in some bowerbirds a glassy turquoise-blue.

We humans get a slightly uncomfortable feeling from eyes that are white or bright yellow, like the barred warbler's, the crowned crane's, the European sparrow-hawk's (Fig. 27), the king vulture's, or the stone curlew's (Fig. 52). The layman is likely, without reason, to give these birds a bad character.

In the very large eyes of owls the variety of colors of the iris is especially striking. The eagle owl and the long-eared owl have fiery yellow-red eyes; the short-eared owl, sulphur-yellow ones; the little owl, amber-yellow; and both the tawny owl and the barn owl, very dark brown ones.

In these normal eyes there is a black layer at the back of the iris; if it is missing the eye looks blue. This blue is a structural color, like the blue in feathers, which is produced when an almost colorless, transparent layer overlies a dark pigment.

Red eyes, which we often find in albino mammals such as white mice and white rabbits, occur when there is no black pigment anywhere in the eye, even behind the retina where it plays an important role in seeing. Red-eyed animals are greatly hampered in bright light. If they live in holes and are dependent mainly on their sense of smell and touch, like the creatures just mentioned, they can manage to get along and even breed. But a bird, which is almost entirely dependent on its eyesight, would have a hard time surviving in these circumstances in the wild. We can be fairly sure that if an albino bird can produce any pigment at all, it will use it to back the retina, where it is so vital.

Hearing

Hearing is apparently well-developed in all birds. The fact that many of them communicate by voice shows this, and the way songbirds and parrots imitate artificial or natural sounds proves that they hear them the same way we do.

Owls, especially the species that hunt mostly at night, hear particularly well. They have all sorts of devices to move their large, slit-shaped ear-openings, and the left and right ear are often very differently shaped. As a result they are able to pinpoint the spot where they hear the tiny sound of a mouse gnawing its food or scuttling about. The feathers covering the opening of the ear are carried on a special flap of skin; when an owl is listening to a sound below, this flap is bent forwards to open the ear and the head it tilted sideways. Since these nocturnal hunters have to be as silent as possible, there is a velvety "fur" on their wings to silence the sound of the wings. Nightjars also have the same sort of device.

It has recently been discovered that the oil-bird, which lives in caves and emerges only at night, uses its voice the same way a bat does. When flying in the caves, it utters a series of clicks and judges from the echo what objects are in its path.

While we are considering the bird's senses, we might mention how it reacts to heat and cold. Most birds can stand fairly extreme cold unless they have naked parts that stick out—long legs, combs, wattles, and the like. If they have, they run the risk of freezing in our climate. This is, of course, especially true of tropical birds.

A bird's toes are particularly likely to freeze in cold

weather. When it is thawing, waterfowl usually sleep standing on the ice; but if it gets colder, they lie down and hide their feet in their belly-feathers. When they are swimming in icy water, they do the same, hiding first one leg and then the other in the feathers. When a grebe wants to warm one foot, it puts it under its wing.

When it is cold, the small waders hop along on one leg, as if the other were missing. Some birds, like gulls, which usually stretch both legs out behind when they fly, hide them in their belly-feathers, bringing them out only to make a turn or to land. Even the long-legged ruffs and cranes draw both feet into their belly-feathers in flight, leaving their tarsal joints sticking out on either side of the tail.

Since birds do not have sweat-glands, their defense against the heat is to open their beaks wide and evaporate water from the throat; they often help the process by panting. The feathers are laid flat, and the wings are raised a little to reduce the insulating layer of air around the body. A bird that is cold, on the other hand, ruffles its feathers so much that its wings are hidden between the feathers of its back and side.

When it is warm and sunny, certain birds have a sun-bathing posture. They spread out their wings and tails in a characteristic way and turn their backs to the sun so that the warm rays can penetrate to the skin through the loosely-held feathers. Lots of other birds such as waterfowl and waders like to sun themselves when it is cold but do not adopt any special posture.

20. Getting About

We do not know whether the first birds were tree-dwellers hopping about the branches or ground animals which later took to the trees. But it is certain that there are some present-day tree-dwelling species whose recent ancestors lived on the ground and some ground-dwellers which have come from tree-dwelling stock.

Some birds like the European swift (Fig. 78) have almost lost the ability to walk or sit on the tarsus—they can only fly, lie down, hang, and make a clumsy attempt at climbing. Most kingfishers, with their little legs and their close-together toes, can hardly get about on flat ground without the help of their wings, and in the wild they do not need to. House martins and crag martins have the same trouble. The barn swallow, however, does fairly well on its feet.

At the other extreme are the flightless birds that cannot do anything but run—the ostrich, kiwi, emu, cassowary, some rails, and the New Zealand owl-parrot or kakapo. Some birds that cannot fly make up for this loss by living in the water; penguins use their wings as paddles, moving them under water even when they themselves are swimming on the surface (Fig. 79). A swimming penguin uses its legs only as rudders; but when it gets on land, it can cover a considerable distance by walking. In contrast to penguins, the grebes and loons—great swimmers both on the surface and under water—have kept the power of flight, but can hardly walk.

Good fliers are generally poor walkers, but there are many exceptions. Many waders, and plovers in particular, are very nimble on foot and on the wing can cover hundreds of miles at a stretch. Pigeons, sandgrouse, larks, and wagtails, which get all their food on the ground, run around busily all the time and are also skilful and untiring fliers.

The way a bird's foot is constructed is closely adapted to the ground it walks on. The toes of Pallas's sandgrouse, which lives in sandy semi-desert, have shrunk so that only a small surface touches the ground (Fig. 80); and the same thing has happened in the horse and the ostrich. On the other hand, birds that run over the leaves of floating plants need long toes that span as great a surface as possible (Figs. 81 and 40*a*).

FIG. 78. Six-weeks-old European swifts, which can fly, hang on a vertical piece of cloth.

FIG. 79. A swimming penguin.

a

b

FIG. 80. The foot of the 10½-ounce Pallas's sandgrouse. One-half natural size. *a* From the side. *b* The bones of the feet seen from above.

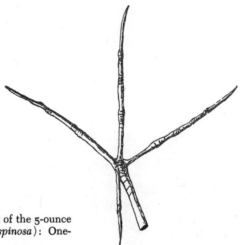

FIG. 81. The foot of the 5-ounce jacana (*Jacana spinosa*): One-half natural size.

Very long legs occur in birds that run fast, like ostriches, in birds that move around in high grass, like the black-winged stilt (Fig. 57*b*), and in herons and flamingos (Fig. 11) which wade out from the shore to catch food. The flamingo jigs about stirring up the mud, its webbed feet keeping it from sinking in too deep; and with its beak held upside down, it strains out tiny bits of animal and plant food, the way a duck does. Herons and flamingos are good fliers, and if you clip their wings they walk about very awkwardly.

When tree-birds walk on the ground, they keep their hopping gait that is adapted for the branches. You have seen house sparrows and European robins and other little birds walk this way; the tree-dwelling toucan, bird of paradise, and hornbill also do the same. The only birds that have gone over to a real walk, in which the feet are set down alternately, are those that spend a lot of time on the ground—wagtails, pipits, starlings, larks, and the ground hornbill. Crows walk rather unsteadily because their toes will not spread far enough apart to give them a good balance. Many birds, like chaffinches, have an unusual mixture of hopping and running that looks something like a polka step. Thrushes can either run or hop.

It is possible that the ancestral passerines were hoppers. At any rate, young larks hop for a time after they have left the nest, although later on they become adept runners. Apparently, at this young age it would take too great an effort to balance their bodies on one leg for the time it takes to make a step.

Climbing

Almost all birds that can climb do it by hopping upwards. Woodpeckers, tree creepers, and woodhewers of the American tropics also use their tails as props. When it is resting, the woodpecker clings to the bark and keeps itself from slipping by propping itself on its tail (Fig. 45); for this purpose the feathers at the tip of the tail are

FIG. 82. A European nuthatch upside down on a tree trunk. One-third natural size.

especially hard and bristly. The special molt of this tail-prop was discussed in Chapter 14.

The European nuthatch does not have a tail-prop but holds onto a vertical surface with its strong feet, toes, and claws. It hops slantwise up a tree, turns around (Fig. 82), and digs at the bark below it; it can also climb while it is upside down. Parrots and crossbills use their beaks to climb; hooking the crooked upper mandible onto a surface, they let go with their feet and draw themselves up.

Flying

Apart from bats, birds are the only living vertebrates that can really fly properly. The bones in the wing of a bird have evolved from the same bones as the front legs of mammals and reptiles, but the wing-bones have been much modified to anchor the large flight-feathers, called primaries and secondaries (Figs. 83 and 5a).

Most birds have ten primaries, which are attached to what corresponds to the hand of mammals. In various passerines the outermost primary is reduced, while grebes and flamingos and some other birds have eleven or twelve. The number of secondaries, which are attached to the ulna (one of the bones of the forearm), is more variable. Hummingbirds and European swifts have only about six, the pelican and some petrels about twenty. Birds also have the remains of a thumb, which is moveable and bears a few feathers. This thumb, which is sometimes called the alula or bastard wing, plays an important part in the flight of certain birds. The relative length of the bones in the wing varies with the way the bird flies.

All the many kinds of bird flight rely on the principle familiar to every little boy who has put his hand out of the window of a moving car: that a flat surface inclined slightly upward to a current of air will be pushed upwards, or, in other words, is able to support a weight. The slower the speed of the air relative to the wing, the less weight can be supported. For a bird to support itself in the

FIG. 83. The longest primaries of two birds which both weigh about 22 pounds. The white feather (17½ inches long) is from a mute swan, which has a flapping flight. The black feather (26½ inches long) is from a condor, which soars.

air, it is not enough that it spread its wings sideways; it must also arrange to pass through the air fast enough to get the necessary lift to balance its weight. If it does not move fast enough, the wing will not give any lift, and we say that it "stalls."

There are various ways a bird can get the necessary forward speed; the simplest is by gliding slightly downward. The downward angle depends greatly on the efficiency of the wing in giving lift; birds' wings have evolved many beautiful adaptations, such as their downward concave shape, which improve these lifting properties and so reduce the downward angle of glide necessary for flight. Gliding in still air always means a loss of height, which in turn means that the bird must have some way of gaining height again.

If the air in which the bird is gliding is itself rising, as does warm air or wind deflected upward from a hill or a

FIG. 84. A golden eagle alighting with its wing-tip feathers spread. Note that the bastard wing is raised.

FIG. 85. A golden eagle soaring. The wing-tips are bent upward showing that they are helping to support the bird in the air.

wave, this movement may carry the bird upward faster than it loses height by gliding; and the net result will be a gain. Birds can also gain height by using the difference between the wind velocity higher up and the velocity close to the surface of the ground or water, where it is slowed down by friction. However it is done, the ability to glide without loss of height is called soaring. Many birds are past masters at it. Some of them, like the vultures and eagles (Figs. 84 and 85), go in for very broad wings and fly relatively slowly; while others like the albatross fly fast and have long narrow wings. Each of these two kinds of soarings wings has its peculiar advantages and disadvantages which fit the habits of their owners. Both kinds allow a great distance to be covered with the expenditure of very little energy, as the birds do not have to flap their wings.

The majority of birds fly in less open places where they cannot rely on upcurrents and the like; instead of gliding downward to get the necessary speed, these birds flap their wings. In flapping-flight most birds use the inner and outer parts of their wings for such different purposes that we can consider them separately. Essentially, the inner part, with the secondaries, is used like the whole wing of a gliding bird—as a lifting surface held obliquely to the air-flow. Although this part is moved when the wings flap, the movement is not an important part of the working of a flapping wing; to make explanations easier, it can be regarded as working like the wing of an airplane, which provides only a lifting surface. The propellers of an airplane provide the speed necessary for the wings to work; and the outer part of a bird's wing, the primary feathers, functions in a very similar way; it beats up and down, twisting at the end of each stroke, so that with each downbeat the bird is pressed forwards.

This simplified picture gives the basic idea of normal flapping flight, but it glosses over the elegant engineering achievements of the wings of certain birds—to say nothing of such complications as how the different parts of the wing are held at the correct angle to the air-flow at the different stages of the wing-beat. Furthermore, the nature of the wing-flap changes drastically when a bird is hovering or alighting or taking off.

The hummingbird also flaps its wings, but they work in a totally different way—more like a helicopter continually driving air downward to support its weight. The wings beat more or less horizontally, and the air is driven downward in the fore-stroke by the lower surface of the wings, in the back-stroke by the upper. While the principle of this kind of flight is easier to understand than that of the pigeon, it is hard to believe that some of these little birds manage to move their wings to and fro sixty times a second. A hummingbird can fly backward, which no other bird can do, although insects can.

The different shapes of wings have different kinds of advantages, and there is no simple answer to the question which bird flies best: it all depends what the bird wants to do. Rapid fliers, which have to cover great distances, have long, narrow, pointed wings, whether they are soarers like the albatross or beat their wings like the plovers, the ducks, or Pallas's sandgrouse (Fig. 86).

Broad-winged birds fly more slowly, and their wings continue to work even when they are traveling at very

FIG. 86. Two wings of the same length (11¾ inches) belonging to birds of the same weight (10½ ounces). Above: the wing of Pallas's sandgrouse, area 29½ square inches. Below: the wing of a female European sparrowhawk, area 45 square inches, i.e., half as large again as the sandgrouse's.

slow speeds and would otherwise stall. The primary feathers of wing-tips stand out separately from one another (Figs. 84, 85, and 86) and are often tapered to increase this effect. The bastard wing also helps to keep a smooth flow of air over the wing and prevent stalling.

All birds that fly, of course, are able to some extent both to flap their wings and to soar, or at least glide. Some, like the peregrine falcon, normally fly by alternately beating their wings and then gliding. Others, like the woodpeckers, wagtails, and many finches, have an undulating flight: they mount for a few moments as they flap their wings, and then with wings folded let their momentum carry them like a bolt in a falling arc.

So far, we have considered only straight flight. A bird may also need to maneuver among thick foliage, whether to avoid pursuit or to pursue. Watch a European jay fly deftly in and out among the branches of a tree, or a European sparrowhawk (Fig. 86) as he falls with lightning speed on a flying prey or with equal suddenness brakes when the little bird dives into a thornbush.

Soaring birds usually have a much larger wing-area, relative to their weight, than flapping birds (Figs. 83 and 86), but size alone has an effect even in birds that fly the same way. Small wings are in fact less efficient than larger one of the same shape, so that smaller birds must have relatively larger wings if they are to use the same kind of flight as larger birds. When geese and gulls fold their wings, the tips of the longest feathers project farther beyond the tail in the smaller species than in their larger relatives; this shows that the smaller birds have a relatively larger wing-area.

The different shapes and sizes of wings and tail correspond to the needs of each species. But remember that a bird is not made just to fly, like an airplane; it has to be able to fold its wings so that they will not hinder its other everyday activities.

a Hummingbird. Three-fourths natural size.

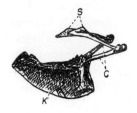

b Budgerigar, which uses a quick flapping flight and does not glide. It has no wishbone. Five-sixths natural size.

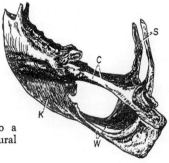

c Pelican. Short keel fused to a huge wishbone. One-fifth natural size.

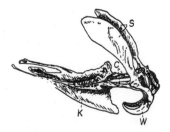

d Black-footed penguin. Broad shoulder blades. One-fourth natural size.

FIG. 87. Various breastbones and shoulder girdles. K = Keel of the breastbone, C = Coracoid bone, W = Wishbone (furcula), S = Shoulder blades (scapulas).

Birds that have to beat their wings all the time they are flying have large breast-muscles, which are attached to a long, deep keel of the breastbone (Figs. 87*a* and *b*). Soaring birds with large wings do not need such large muscles, but depend more on their bones and tendons to save their strength. Such birds have the breastbone, "wishbone," and the large coracoid bones of the shoulder girdle forming a single framework, to which the relatively small muscles are attached rather far forward (Fig. 87*c*).

The flight muscles of birds like pigeons, which fly for long stretches, are red. The gallinaceous birds and the tinamous, which have powerful muscles and small wings to lift them quickly away from danger, have white breast muscles for hard work that does not last long. The white muscles of these birds are highly developed, sometimes amounting to about one-third of the body weight. Think of the white breast meat of a roast turkey and compare it with the red meat of its legs, which are designed for continual walking. The red breast muscles of captive birds degenerate if they are not used, but this does not happen in the white-muscled birds which, in nature, often go all day without using their wings.

The speed of a bird relative to the surrounding air has been measured in many species, although without instruments it is easy to overestimate. Most smallish birds seem to fly between 20 and 40 mph, larger ones frequently up to 50 mph. A few top speeds for horizontal flight may be mentioned: the mallard, the golden plover, a hummingbird, and the common swift have been recorded at around 60 mph, a teal at 74 mph, and an American swift (*Chaetura*) at 89 mph. In a dive, of course, a bird may travel considerably faster than in level flight, and it may also be able to put on a spurt when it is pursued. A European cormorant trying to escape an airplane was clocked at 65 mph, but a wild goose that was being pursued in the same way could not do more than 56 mph. A homing pigeon

FIG. 89. Mallard feet with the webs folded and with the webs spread out.

ashore and only enters the water if it is absolutely forced to. When a bird gets water in its wing-pockets or under its wings, it makes a few bathing movements and then stands up in the water and flaps its wings vigorously to shake out the drops. Land birds and marsh birds do the same thing when they bathe in dust or water.

Since a bird which has its feathers is much lighter than water, it easily floats. You often hear people exclaim of tiny ducklings, "Look, they can swim already!" Such people do not realize that even a dead duckling will not sink if it has enough oil on it. While it is not surprising that a duckling can float, it is amazing that it can dive before it is an hour old, for diving requires skill as well as a lot of work with the feet to stay under. As soon as the duckling stops kicking, it pops up to the surface like a cork.

Even species that rarely dive when they are grown-up practice diving when they are a few hours old. One gets the idea that they do this as a protection against the moment when a bird of prey may show up.

Swimming, a bird moves its feet alternately, as when walking. When the foot is brought forward, the web and toes are folded together and the toe joints bent, so that the leg can move almost without resistance from the water; very good swimmers have legbones that are flattened on the sides so as to be almost knife-like. When the feet are moved backward, the toes and webs are fully spread (Fig. 89), and the strong muscles of the legs drive the body swiftly forward. You can see how strong these legs are by picking up a diving duck: it will paddle so vigorously on the empty air that it may even sprain its tarsal joint.

The only swimmer that goes about things differently is the mute swan, and that only when it is threatening. It then paddles with both feet at the same time, and with each mighty stroke the water foams up against its breast. It may be added that this kind of swimming gets it along no faster than the bird it is pursuing, which hurries away with feathers laid flat and legs paddling alternately.

Most birds start a dive by first jumping slightly out of the water. A lot of them, however, let themselves sink slowly by pressing their wings and feathers close to their bodies, and presumably also by emptying the air sacs to make themselves less buoyant; then, with head and neck under water, they give a vigorous kick upward. Fishing birds stick their heads under the water so that they can look for their food without being bothered by ripples and reflections on the surface.

Penguins are almost the only birds which use their wings to swim on the surface. Underwater a few marine diving ducks and the dipper use both wings and legs. The auks, murres, and penguins use only their wings when they dive, holding their legs out behind them to steer. Grebes, loons, and most diving ducks keep their wings in their watertight pockets when they are under water.

European cormorants, which have big wings and lack the special feather-pockets, hold their wings slightly out when they are under water, but do not use them to propel themselves. For this reason they do not rest on the water, going there only to bathe or fish. As soon as they have finished, they go ashore and hold their wings out for some minutes to dry, looking like an eagle on a coat of arms (Fig. 90).

Pelicans, which are relatives of the European cormorant, do not have any feather pockets either; when they swim, they hold their wings up out of the water in a strange way. The whole skin of large pelicans is cushioned with air, and they are so buoyant that they are not able to dive at all. The brown pelicans, together with the terns and certain kingfishers, are plunge-divers: they fly along above the water and plummet down when they see their prey, staying under water only for a few seconds. The osprey does the same thing, but instead of taking the fish in its beak as the others do, it grabs it with its claws. The best plunge-diver of all is the gannet, which dives from a considerable height straight into the sea. Since its nostrils are blocked up (Fig. 91), the impact of its dive does not force any water into its lungs.

Penguins are better adapted than any other bird for swimming and diving. Because they have no land enemies, the penguins have been able to lose their power of flight

FIG. 90. European cormorants, back from fishing, dry their wings.

FIG. 91. The adult gannet is white, the youngster brown flecked with white.

and adapt their bodies mainly to life in the water. The wings have turned into fins with powerful breast muscles to work them. The breastbone and the shoulder girdle are much like a flying bird's, except for the tremendous shoulder blades (Fig. 87*d*). By giving up feather-pockets and air-filled bones, a penguin has lost much of a bird's typical buoyancy; even when it rests quietly on the surface it sinks in up to its back (Fig. 79) and can use its wings to swim just as well as when under water.

The length of time birds stay under water, and how fast and how deep they go, depends on what they do there: some hunt swift fish, others tear water-plants and mussels from the sea bottom. We know that penguins can swim more than 30 feet per second under water.

We have pretty reliable figures for the time some diving birds spend under water. If you want to check these, be sure to keep a watch in your hand, for otherwise you are sure to overestimate. Many diving ducks usually stay under for a half to three-quarters of a minute—although if you are waiting for the duck to come up, it seems a lot longer. The mergansers and the loons, which eat fish, and the scoters, which eat mussels, do not seem to have any trouble staying under water for as long as two minutes, although they usually come up after one. Most birds have a certain depth to which they normally dive—usually from 3 to 10 feet—and at which they find their principal food. The coot and the dipper have the shallowest and shortest dives and may be considered the poorest divers. The best are the European cormorants, grebes, loons, mergansers, marine diving ducks, and above all the penguins. Eiders, European cormorants, and penguins have been recorded down to 60 feet. People are sometimes misled by reports that fishermen have pulled birds out of the lower meshes of nets more than 150 feet below the surface of the sea. These birds may have got tangled up as the nets were let down or pulled up.

The true ducks can be divided into the dabbling ducks, which find their food either on the surface or immediately beneath it, and the diving ducks, dumpier birds which float flat on the water, get their food by submerging completely under water, and are recognizable by a strongly lobed hind toe. All swans, geese, and ducks can dive to some extent, the adult mute swan only with the greatest difficulty.

Different birds have different ways of diving, and we must remember that flying and diving make opposite demands on a bird. To fly, one must be light and have big wings; to dive, one must be as heavy as possible in order to remain underwater. The best thing for a diving specialist would obviously be to stop flying, and this is just what some birds have done: the penguins, the extinct great auks, two steamer ducks, one grebe, and the Galapagos cormorant. These birds could afford to lose their flight because they live mostly where there is little danger from land enemies.

21. *Mental Powers of Birds*

People who see a bird acting out his instincts often take it as a sign of understanding or cleverness: they think that the bird is making rational use of its own past experience. But these instincts are inborn and in the bird's natural surroundings help preserve the species.

Animal lovers do not like to think that any animal, especially their own, can be stupid. We might as well explain straight away that the words "clever" and "stupid" refer only to degrees of mental ability, and do not imply any judgment of the bird. We should try to avoid words that suggest moral judgment, but ordinary language has almost nothing but these loaded words to describe mental and emotional states; as a result, misunderstandings and warped ideas can sometimes arise.

Birds that live on open plains need different mental qualities from forest-dwellers or water birds; once we realize this, it becomes clear that in all three groups there are clever birds and stupid ones. A species may be as well served by its ability to fly or swim well as by a highly developed brain or by being able to rear countless offspring.

Man, being largely dependent on his intelligence, naturally thinks that a well-developed brain represents the highest kind of existence. But if a murre or a grebe had to pass judgment on us, we should come off pretty poorly. For their highest aspirations would be to keep watertight and to dive well, and their preen gland is for them what our brain is for us, if I may make my point by exaggerating a little. For a partridge or an auk it is no disgrace to be stupid. If you were as stupid as a partridge, you would simply have to lay sixteen eggs a year to keep the species from dying out; and if you were a distinguished diver with plumage so watertight that you could spend your whole life, day and night, in the storms and rains of polar seas, you would not need much intelligence.

In general, birds tend to be clever when they have to adjust themselves to so many different situations that they cannot become one-sided specialists. Sparrows and crows, for example, have become very intelligent, as birds go. They quickly learn to tell what is important and what is not; in addition, they have an enormous curiosity, because they eat almost anything and in our climate have to keep going in extremes of heat and cold when food and shelter may be difficult to find.

What we call sociability or family feeling in humans is at least as well developed in birds that live together and raise their young together. This feeling helps the survival of the species. Of course, the term "family feeling" suggests something beautiful and moving, and we find ourselves making another moral judgment. When we say that a pair of geese care for their children in a "touching" fashion and that they defend them with "self-sacrificing love," or that the adult geese stay together all their lives "with unswerving fidelity," the words imply praise, for we all do these things ourselves—at least we ought to. But remember that birds know how to look after their young without being told; they have a strong urge to protect them, and strive to do what is necessary in spite of every obstacle. A bird has no parental duties, only parental pleasures; one might say it looks after its young for the fun of it. In response to certain stimuli, birds have evolved habits that are curiously like our own actions based on morality and reason. As we pursue our studies of the behavior of birds, we come more and more to recognize that our own behavior toward our family and strangers, the emotions of love and hate, are in some ways a much simpler business than we imagine.

The bird is far from being a simple reflex machine. His life is, to a certain extent, a chain of instinctive activities, but the chain is not quite complete; gaps have to be filled by the individual's use of his own experience. The more gaps there are, the better the opportunity for intelligence to work.

The mental gifts of the average bird are pretty far behind those of the average mammal, but it is not easy to devise sensible tests to judge intelligence. For one thing, we can only compare species that have the same kind of habits. A couple of examples will show this. Suppose you raise some partridges from the egg so that they are completely tame, and train them to come to your finger when you tap it on the floor (which corresponds roughly to the way their parents call them to eat). If you tap on a windowsill, they will hesitate a little and then fly up to it. They consider the wall as an upward continuation of the floor and have the sense to use their wings to get to the sill. But if you tap on the table, they will run to a spot on the floor beneath, growing greatly confused; no number of trials will teach them to fly up to the table, even if you repeatedly put them there and allow them to walk about, or if they happen to land there when they are flying around the ceiling.

Hand-reared partridges will become very attached to you, but if you want to keep them from following you through an open door into the next room, all you have to do is to put a piece of wire-netting 18 inches high across the door. They will keep running up and down in front of this obstacle without every trying to fly over it, which they could easily do. A pheasant, a black grouse, or a

capercaillie would very quickly take a couple of steps
backwards and fly onto the fence and so to the other
side. These three birds habitually fly up into trees in
the wild, and they use this innate ability, which the partridges do not have, in the new situation. To a person
who does not know their natural habits, the partridge will
seem a lot more stupid than the others; but this conclu-
sion is not justified.

It is different when we compare graylag geese and
cranes. These birds both inhabit roughly the same sort
of terrain, and neither of them perches in trees; they use
their wings mainly to fly long distances. Some cranes I
raised went eight years without learning that they could
not go through a three-foot-high fence of wire-netting. If
I led them behind it or they landed there after a flight,
they would try desperately, over and over again, to get
through the wire. Geese in the same circumstances very
quickly fly over fences that are even higher. In this sense
one can say that geese are cleverer than cranes. If you
repeat the experiment with geese, they start each time
by trying to push through but in each successive trial they
spend less and less time doing this before flying over the
obstacle. Evidently, one successful solution is not enough,
as it often is for man, apes, and dogs, to insure that no
more mistakes are made.

Young jackdaws which have been reared in a big wire
cage, where they can fly, exhibit fear the first time you
leave the door open for them. If you manage to attract
them outside, they will keep trying to get back home
through the wire, until finally they chance upon the door
and enter. You have to repeat this again and again before
they learn to use the door as a matter of course. If they
nest inside the cage and the door is left open, they will
fly in and out to gather food for their young. But when
the young have left the nest and one of them sits begging
in some corner of the cage away from the door—even on
top of the nesting place—the parents try to fly directly

to it from outside the cage and have to learn again to use the door.

People who keep canaries may also have noticed how difficult it is for these birds to change their habits. A bird that is allowed to fly about the room will have a great deal of trouble finding its way back into its cage if you turn the cage half round while it is outside.

Another example shows how little insight a bird has into its own actions. If you keep a dozen adult mute swans on a pond, one pair will in the spring set themselves up as the rulers of the pond and will not let the others into the water. The unlucky birds lie around on the shore all the time and hardly dare to eat or drink. If you go down to the pond and carry away the tyrants under the very eyes of the other swans, they still do not enter the water. After several hours one or another becomes so thirsty that it dares go to the water; then, as it is not chased away by the tyrant pair, it swims about a little, taking care at first to keep near the protecting bank. It may be half a day or more before the rest venture to join it.

Even more striking is the mental helplessness of one of these swans when it is walking over the ice during a thaw. If it comes to a puddle on the ice in which the water is only a fraction of an inch deep, it squats down and with a great pushing of feet tries to swim across. Geese and ducks would simply walk straight through. Birds are obviously creatures of many instincts and little intelligence.

In the types that are mentally most developed, like the raven, we find the first traces of what seems to be insight into their instinctive behavior. All the crow family instinctively hide bits of food; the youngsters in the nest begin to do this without having seen other birds do it. An adult jackdaw is not very clever and will placidly hide a piece of food right before the eyes of its keeper or of other jackdaws, so that the concealment rather loses its point. But the raven learns very early in life to take its booty secretly to a nook it seldom visits. At a moment when nobody is looking, it flies noiselessly away to its hiding place, and even suppresses the cry it normally gives when it is about to take off.

People often confuse a bird that has a good memory with a clever one. But memory is only one requirement for intelligence. Some birds come back every spring to the same nesting place although there are others equally suitable close by: they must remember the old site. European nutcrackers hide nuts in the ground in autumn and dig them up in the winter and spring when they run out of food. They seem to retain a remarkably accurate idea of the positions of their many food-stores, even under a foot or two of snow. For such birds a good memory must be a matter of life and death.

22. How Does a Bird Find Its Way?

There is no doubt that migrating birds find their way about the world with remarkable accuracy. The greater shearwater ranges the Atlantic from the Arctic Circle to Cape Horn, assembling every year at the tiny islands of Tristan da Cunha in the South Atlantic, its only known breeding place. The banding of thousands of birds of other species has shown that many of them return year after year to the same piece of woodland, cliff, or marsh, even to the identical nesting site.

Many ingenious explanations have been put forward to explain how these birds find their way back. Although none of these seems entirely correct, at least we know something about how birds do and do not navigate. It is out of the question, for example, that regular migrations are the result of the birds being passively drifted by the winds. Although winds may alter the number of migrants at a particular place, migration is an active striving to get to a certain place or to fly in a certain direction.

Many migrant species in captivity become restless at the migration seasons, especially at those times when their wild fellows are on the move. This unrest is not simply the result of their seeing or hearing their own species flying overhead, although sociable birds are especially attracted to join a flock of their own kind.

In birds that have strong family bonds, like geese, the parents may guide the young on their first migrations so that migration routes become traditional. But this cannot be so in those like the European cuckoo, whose young migrate some weeks after their parents have left.

Many experiments have been made in which migrants were transported off their normal line of migration, banded, and released. Such experiments with large numbers of starlings in the autumn demonstrated that the young birds tended to resume their migration parallel to their original course—they maintained their original direction just as if they had not been transplanted. The adult birds, however, set off in a different direction, towards the areas where they had previously wintered. Evidently, the young birds knew only that they must migrate in a particular direction, while the adults had learned the actual wintering area and could fly to it.

Many birds have this ability to home to a familiar area, but in some it appears to be very poorly developed. People who train pigeons for racing find that familiarity with landmarks helps a bird to find its way home; experimenters therefore tried releasing birds in places where they could not possibly have been before, even on migration. One of the most spectacular journeys was that of a manx shearwater which returned from Boston, Massachusetts, to its nest on the island of Skokholm, off the coast of Wales. This bird covered 3050 miles in 12½ days, arriving 10 hours before the boat that brought the letter announcing its release.

In preparation for a long-distance race pigeon-breeders train their birds to fly in a particular direction over longer and longer stretches, and for some time the ability of pigeons to home without practice was doubted. It has now been shown, however, that under the right conditions pigeons can home from any direction through unknown country, and without being trained.

The means by which pigeons and other birds know what direction to fly is by no means certain. It seems, however, that for those species that travel by day the sun serves as a guide. If such birds are released in sunny weather, they set off in approximately the right direction; but if it is overcast, they go off to all points of the compass. One of the difficulties of using the sun to navigate is its continual motion, but it appears that birds can allow for this movement, as if they had chronometers like a ship's navigator.

Migrating birds do not stop traveling in overcast weather unless the cloud closes right down; they must use secondary clues, such as landmarks, to maintain their direction. Migrants are much affected by the topography of the land, especially when they are flying fairly low with contrary winds. Chaffinches crossing the flat plain of northern Europe are deflected along coastlines, and in more hilly country an escarpment will help to channel them unless it would take them too far off their preferred course.

Some large birds like storks and birds of prey make use of rising columns of warm air to help them along during their migration. They soar up in spirals on one column and then glide down to the foot of the next. In consequence their migration routes are determined partly by the position of these upcurrents.

In November you may have heard the sibilant calls of redwings (a type of thrush) migrating overhead. Many thrushes and warblers, as well as other birds, travel at night; and we are at a loss to understand how they can navigate. Although on a clear night landmarks must be almost as conspicuous as during the day, there is no sun from which the birds can get their bearings. Recent experiments, however, have shown that blackcaps and garden warblers that have been raised indoors and never before seen the sky can get their bearings at migration time by the stars alone. These tame birds have been known to try to hop out of their cages in the direction in which their wild companions are migrating. If clouds cover the sky, however, the warblers lose their sense of direction.

In the last years there have been tremendous advances in our knowledge about homing and migration. There is still a great way to go, however, before we can understand how millions of birds every year fly hundreds and thousands of miles, many of them for the first time, without anyone to guide them.

It is to be hoped that the reader of these pages will have realized that while a great deal is already known about the life of birds, many of the biggest problems are only beginning to be solved.

INDEX

Available in

ANN ARBOR SCIENCE LIBRARY
OR
ANN ARBOR SCIENCE PAPERBACKS

THE STARS *by W. Kruse and W. Dieckvoss*

THE ANTS *by Wilhelm Goetsch*

THE SENSES *by Wolfgang von Buddenbrock*

LIGHT: VISIBLE AND INVISIBLE *by Eduard Ruechardt*

THE BIRDS *by Oskar and Katharina Heinroth*

EBB AND FLOW: THE TIDES OF EARTH, AIR, AND WATER
by Albert Defant

ANIMAL CAMOUFLAGE *by Adolf Portmann*

PLANET EARTH *by Karl Stumpff*

VIRUS *by Wolfhard Weidel*

THE SUN *by Karl Kiepenheuer*

THE UNIVERSITY OF MICHIGAN PRESS